FOREWORD

The period covered by this report is one of the most significant in the history of Britain's railways because the main network and associated operations have been restructured to a form never previously seen. Even before 1923, when there were 120 plus companies, they were generally 'vertically integrated' on a geographic basis, with core functions handled in-house.

On 1 April 1994, the newly formed company, Railtrack, was given ownership of the main network infrastructure. Following earlier recommendations by the Health and Safety Commission, they were also given overall primary responsibility for safety on their network. The remainder of the industry, initially still owned by British Rail, was divided into over 100 separate units, some dealing with the day-to-day running of trains, and others competing for overhaul of trains, maintenance and renewal of infrastructure, technical and commercial services etc. Notwithstanding Railtrack's special role, each of these companies has its own legal responsibilities for safety. At present just a few of these units are in private hands, but by the time of the next Annual Safety Report, a major part of the industry is likely to be privately owned.

While privatisation of the railways is expected to provide opportunities, the process of change is inevitably accompanied by uncertainties and risks too if it is not managed properly. Change brings the potential for major new investment on the railways. The industry is aware that parts of the existing network are in need of substantial modernisation. Existing levels of safety are being maintained but where modernisation is required, this is being done by judicious management and maintenance of the system. There is a limit to the extent to which such measures can be applied effectively. It is essential that when that limit is being approached decisions are taken to renew or upgrade those parts of the system concerned. Such investments in the network will not only have the benefit of providing a better service but will also enhance safety, both by providing new train control systems and the opportunity for new rolling stock. There are already a number of major initiatives under consideration aimed at improving and developing the existing rail network. Well known examples are the Channel Tunnel Rail Link and redevelopment of the West Coast Main Line.

If the full benefit of such initiatives is to be achieved without detriment to safety in this restructured railway where many more companies will be pressing their own interests, the industry must collectively take steps to ensure that the safety management system is complete, cohesive and totally effective. It is crucially important that those who have responsibility for safety clearly understand their duties and make the necessary investment of effort and resources to carry them out. Moreover they must co-operate with all other parties with whom they interface to ensure the safety of their employees and the public.

Another recommendation of the Health and Safety Commission, now implemented, provides the necessary tool to enable the Inspectorate to determine how well duty holders are meeting their responsibilities. I refer to the Railways (Safety Case) Regulations 1994 which came into force on 28 February 1994. The Railway Safety Case prepared by Railtrack and accepted by HSE specifies how all safety-related activities on the network will be managed and controlled. It also illustrates how Railtrack will assess the safety cases of all independent operators on its infrastructure.

The main strategy being employed by HM Railway Inspectorate to regulate safety within this geographically and managerially diverse industry is to monitor closely, using our increased core of field inspectors, the performance of all the role players. The inspectors check the actual performance and the effectiveness of the management regimes against the commitments and goals in the safety cases. Effective controls must be maintained and the Inspectorate will not hesitate to use its extensive enforcement powers to ensure that they are.

The question of how safety is faring in this rapidly changing scene comes naturally to mind. The overall picture drawn from the data shows little change from recent years. Fluctuations, such as they are, provide no statistically significant messages. However, as you will see, the levels of fatalities and injuries offer no room for complacency. Excluding trespassers and suicides, 42 people died in the running of the railways, which represents two more than last year. They were 17 passengers, nine staff and 16 other persons.* The number of significant train accidents (those which are potentially most dangerous to passengers), for the national system (BR/Railtrack) has fallen this year by eight to 110 in 259 million train miles, giving a rate of 0.42 per million train miles.

If accidents on metropolitan railways and tramways are included in an overall calculation of significant train accidents, the total number shows an increase on last year of nine to 151 in 304 million train miles. This gives a rate of 0.5 per million train miles. I am keen to keep a separate focus in future on tramway figures to avoid distortion of the significant train accident statistics. (The Railway Safety Annual Report for 1993/94 included the figures for the first year's operation of Manchester Metrolink.) The risk to trams ('trains' in legal terms) in the 'street running' environment will inevitably lead to the inclusion of 'road traffic accidents' (RTAs) so there is a risk that the railway records will become confused if we do not keep these statistics separate. Tables 2 and 2A illustrate the differences between such all-inclusive figures (less minor railways) and those of the national (non-metropolitan) network. It is my intention to deal with tramway/LRT statistics in a separate part of the report next year.

This year has been witness to two tragic accidents where passenger trains collided: at Cowden and at Ais Gill. Both of these are described in greater detail in the text of the report and the Cowden collision, leading to the death of two passengers and three railway employees, was the subject of a public inquiry and report. An act of vandalism at Branchton, Strathclyde derailed a passenger train, causing the death of a passenger and the driver. Two youths are each serving 15 year jail sentences for culpable homicide.

There were 61 fewer reports of vandalism than in the year 1993/94, but there were still 228 instances, mainly (131) obstruction of the line. Indeed, the day after the Branchton outrage, two further significant obstructions were placed on running lines in Scotland. The Railway Industry Advisory Committee, which I have the pleasure to chair, is currently examining vandalism and trespass together with other interested parties.

During the year HM Railway Inspectorate was called upon to become deeply involved in monitoring the management of railway signalling during the dispute between signal workers and Railtrack. This involved field inspectors in 175 visits to signal-boxes and the investigation of 118 written complaints. Another unforeseen commitment was our considerable involvement, together with other parts of HSE, in investigating the collapse, at London Heathrow Airport, of part of a tunnel for the Heathrow Express service. The repercussions were more far-reaching than the environs of the airport, however, because the same tunnelling technique, the New Austrian Tunnelling Method, was being employed at several other sites in the building of the Jubilee Line extension. Above these works were located various notable railway stations such as Waterloo and London Bridge. Therefore before authorising a resumption of these works, a particularly thorough assessment of the situation had to be undertaken.

As a part of the Government's strategy for reducing the burden of legislation on industry, this year included work by HSE on the revision of the Reporting of Incidents, Diseases and Dangerous Occurrences Regulations (RIDDOR), to include the Railways (Notice of Accidents) Order, so that only one set of accident reporting regulations should apply to the railways from 1 April 1996. Preparation began of a new publication entitled *Railway safety principles and guidance*, an eight part replacement for the Inspectorate's well known 'Requirements' or 'Blue Book'. These are being developed jointly with the industry and will, for the first time, cover rolling stock and tramways. The documents will be published during 1996.

Public services through the Channel Tunnel were inaugurated during the year. These included both the short distance 'Shuttle' trains for lorries, touring coaches and motor cars, operated by Eurotunnel between Folkestone (Cheriton) and Calais (Coquelles), and the high speed 'Eurostar' services operated jointly by European Passenger Services (EPS), SNCF (French National Railways) and SNCB (Belgian National Railways) between London (Waterloo) and Paris (Nord) and Brussels (Zuid). Much adverse publicity attended a motor car fire on board a train during loading at the terminal, the derailment of another 'Shuttle' train and some minor unit failures. Many of the minor failures stem from systems that are much more complex than those found on ordinary trains. Now that these systems have settled down and

---

* The 16 other persons included 13 level crossing users, two pedestrians crossing tramways and one car driver whose car left a motorway, landed on a rail line and was subsequently struck by a train

HSE
Health & Safety
Executive

RAILWAY
SAFETY

*HM Chief Inspecting Officer of Railways' Annual Report
on the safety record of the railways
in Great Britain during 1994/95*

HSE BOOKS

ISBN 0 7176 1047 0

Front cover: A Metrolink tram at St Peter's Square, Manchester

CONTENTS

the crews have become entirely familiar with the equipment, a more frequent and reliable service has developed.

Following extensive trials of two automatic train protection (ATP) systems (one fitted on the Great Western Main Line, the other on the Chiltern Line), BRB sent the Secretary of State (SoS) for Transport a report of a study which costed the installation of this quality of ATP throughout the network. The report suggested that network-wide fitment would not be cost effective. The SoS asked the Health and Safety Commission for its comments on the report and the Commission sought the views of the Inspectorate. The final comments of the Commission, which are reproduced in Appendix 12 of this report, broadly concurred with the views of the BR study with regard to the ATP system in question. However it will be seen that the Commission continues to press for the implementation of controls that will reduce the number of signals passed at Danger (SPAD). The Inspectorate has not ruled out the possibility of a simpler and more cost effective

form of ATP, which some might see as an enhanced automatic warning system, being developed. I would certainly like to see manufacturers taking up this challenge.

Once again I thank all those in the railway industry who have striven to maintain and improve safety for their efforts. I am sure they will not relax their efforts in the challenging times ahead. Also I thank colleagues in HSE for numerous acts of support over the year, in particular my Railway Inspectorate colleagues for their diligence throughout the year and support to me personally. They have produced this report with their usual enthusiasm and they will ensure that the Inspectorate fully meets the challenge presented by the new railway era.

S S J ROBERTSON

OUTLINE OF THE REPORT

The annual reports on railway safety in Great Britain have long been a useful tool for those professionally involved in the railway industry. They record not only the number of statutorily reportable accidents occurring, categorised under various headings that permit trends to be identified, but also mention, where appropriate, the action being taken to prevent a recurrence.

Written in its current format, the report is a unique publication and the statistics are used by British and foreign governments and companies. The data covering the last 20 to 30 years are in constant demand and requests are regularly received from Britain and overseas.

The report is produced under the Agency Agreement between the Health and Safety Commission and the Secretary of State for Transport mentioned in the Introduction. It records those accidents that have occurred on the railways and tramways in Great Britain which are reportable under the Railways (Notice of Accidents) Order 1986 (SI 1986 No 2187). Certain dangerous occurrences, reportable under the Reporting of Injuries, Diseases and Dangerous Occurrences Regulations 1985 (RIDDOR) (SI 1985 No 2023) are also recorded.

Readers will learn that HM Railway Inspectorate is now bigger than at any time since George Stephenson suggested its establishment in 1840. The 'Father of Railways', as he is sometimes called, was keen to ensure that there was an impartial body of engineers to inspect the burgeoning private railways of the time and to report to the Government on their activities. Today, the Inspectorate, as part of HSE, continues the task of inspecting new works, investigating accidents and reporting safety performance to the Secretary of State for Transport. New legislation has been introduced to ensure the safety of railway operations during the present day revolution; the Inspectorate is monitoring compliance.

Chapter 1 reviews the Railway Inspectorate's activities during the year from 1 April 1994 to 31 March 1995 and gives details of our staffing and structure. It also outlines those aspects of our work that are of particular importance, such as approval of works, level crossing modernisation, automatic train protection (ATP) and the Railway Industry Advisory Committee (RIAC). The Railway, Maritime and Transport Trades Union called signalmen out on a series of strikes, giving the Inspectorate the task of checking the competence of the signalling managers who were put to work in signal-boxes to replace those on strike.

Accidents to people are dealt with in Chapter 2. Of most concern to the public is passenger safety. To interpret the figures given in the report, it is important to define the types of accident which can lead to injury and death:

- **Train accidents** are accidents **to trains** and rolling stock; they include collisions, derailments, running into obstructions and fires in trains.

- **Movement accidents** are accidents **to people**, caused by the movement of railway vehicles but excluding those involved in train accidents, eg being struck by a train when standing too close to a platform edge.

- **Non-movement accidents** are accidents **to people** on railway premises but not connected with the movement of railway vehicles, eg falling on a stairway at a station.

In this report, death and injury to suicides and other trespassers are shown in Appendices 8 and 8A. These figures are not included in the other totals.

Seventeen passengers were killed last year: three in train accidents, 12 in movement accidents (including five from slam doors), and two in non-movement accidents. This is an increase of one over the previous year, and the total of 42 killed (17 passengers, nine staff and 16 other persons) is an increase of two over the same period.

Train accidents, ie accidents involving trains and moving railway vehicles, are dealt with in Chapter 3, where it is noted that the total of 907 train accidents was 70 less than during the previous year.

Significant train accidents are those that are actually or potentially most dangerous to passengers, whether or not they result in casualties. They include most collisions and all derailments on or affecting passenger lines and are shown, in Figure 4, expressed as a rate per million train miles. This annual figure has long been regarded as a reliable index of passenger safety.

Level crossings, where ill-disciplined road transport shares a small piece of ground with high-speed trains, are an anachronism. Eleven types of level crossing are recognised by statute. Although there is regulation in every case, at its most rudimentary, the onus is placed entirely on the road user, most of whom are not professional drivers. When one considers the potential for collision, it is remarkable that there are so few accidents at level crossings. However, with the huge and sustained growth of road transport, safety at the road and railway interface will increasingly depend on the replacement of level crossings with bridges and the education of the road user about the crossings which remain.

Thirteen members of the public were killed in accidents on level crossings last year and there were 60 accidents in total, six fewer than the previous year. Reference is made in more detail to some of these accidents in Chapter 4 and research into road user behaviour is mentioned in Chapter 12.

Three hundred and five fires were reported on the railways last year, a reduction of 17% over the previous year. Chapter 5 contains details of accidental fires and arson on trains and in buildings.

Failures of permanent way and works and of locomotives and rolling stock are shortcomings having the potential to cause accidents. Chapter 6 is a wide-ranging section of the report, recording increases in certain areas but notable reductions in both of the most recently introduced aspects of this chapter, namely wrong side signalling failures (WSF) by 12% and signals passed at Danger (SPAD) by 8%.

Chapter 7 reports on the opening of the Channel Tunnel to public service. This was, of course, the most important event of the century for British transport. Predictably, services have quickly become popular and mass demand will respond to the introduction of attractive fares. Public attention has regrettably been diverted by 'teething troubles' and the financial plight of Eurotunnel which should not detract from the magnitude of the work they have done.

London Underground, with 245 miles of route, is by far the biggest of the metropolitan railways of Great Britain and historically has been an example to the world. Although it is not involved in the fundamental process of public auction currently occupying the national railway, it has put certain non-railway functions, such as staff catering, advertising and car parks out to franchise. Details of its activities for the year are given in Chapter 8.

The dawning of a new tramway era, albeit under the generic title of 'Light rail', has been greeted with enthusiasm by many and has already been adopted by several towns and cities. The most recently approved, South Yorkshire Supertram, opened for public service during the year, as did the Beckton extension of the Docklands Light Railway (DLR). Details of these and other events can be found in Chapter 9.

Great Britain is no longer unique in having a large number of minor railways, most of which are small lines preserved by enthusiasts and sometimes called 'heritage railways'. An impressive selection of lines have also been reinstated in Europe and the USA. Britain still has a leading role in negotiation over legislation affecting these railways. No other body knows this subject better than the Association of Independent Railways (AIR) and the Association of Railway Preservation Societies (ARPS) and it demonstrates that these highly motivated volunteers have much to offer in their field. Chapter 10 deals with the minor railways.

Although railways are acknowledged to be a safe means of transport, many of those who have to maintain them, especially those working on the track, are required to frequent hazardous locations. The degree of that danger may be judged by reference to Chapter 11. Nine railway or contractors' staff were killed during the year, one more than in 1993/94, underlining the lesson that one must never cease to be aware of surrounding dangers.

As noted in Chapter 12, on research, the Inspectorate is now studying the results of a research project it commissioned into the behaviour of road users at level crossings. It is of concern to note from the reports of interviews carried out during this project, the degree of ignorance of drivers who had failed to stop when legally required to do so.

Vandalism continues to be a widespread national problem and the railways, by their nature largely open and unprotected, suffer more than most. Some incidents of vandalism are recorded in Chapter 13, but it also notes a decrease in reported attacks from 289 to 228. However, the fact is that deaths of passengers or staff can result from any such attack.

The Appendices at the end of the report detail the totals of accidents reported by the railways and tramways during the year.

INTRODUCTION

This report, as did those in the past, provides an overview of those matters which affect safety on the railway. Clearly accidents, dangerous occurrences and various failures feature large, for it is this information which provides the safety performance indicators for the industry. But it also provides an insight into the workings of the Railway Inspectorate and the issues which influence its policies and methods of operation.

A major portion of the Inspectorate's work is driven by the Agency Agreement that the Department of Transport has made with the Health and Safety Commission (HSC). This is described in paragraphs 1 to 3.

It must be emphasised that this report only covers events in the year 1 April 1994 to 31 March 1995. Apart from any mentioned in the Chief Inspecting Officer's foreword, reports about railway safety which have appeared in the media, mainly from August 1995, are not commented on in this report.

Agency Agreement

1   Under the agreement, the Health and Safety Executive (HSE), on behalf of the Commission, carries out certain functions for the Secretary of State through HM Railway Inspectorate (HMRI).

2   The Chief Inspecting Officer of Railways advises the Secretary of State on behalf of the Health and Safety Commission and Executive on matters concerned with these functions. Among these functions are the making of level crossing orders, the approval of new railway works, the receipt of notices of accidents given under the Railways (Notice of Accidents) Order 1986, some duties under the Channel Tunnel Act 1987 and the preparation of this report.

3   The Secretary of State receives advice and information from the Commission in connection with these duties, on matters of health and safety and on technical matters relating to railways, tramways, underground and light railways and any other guided passenger transit systems.

Jurisdiction

4   The regulatory Acts and the procedures under which they are applied to ensure railway safety are listed in Appendix 11.

5   Apart from the infrastructure owned by Railtrack (RT) and the operating units of the British Railways Board, there are other major undertakings, principally the metropolitan railways: London Underground Limited, the Strathclyde Metropolitan Railway, the Docklands Light Railway and the Tyne and Wear Metro. In addition, there are some 230 minor railways which were either built with statutory authority or have a gauge exceeding 350 mm or both. The tram systems at Blackpool, Manchester and Sheffield are also within the jurisdiction of HM Railway Inspectorate.

6   All these railways are obliged to report to the Railway Inspectorate all accidents notifiable under railway or health and safety legislation. These accidents and failures are tabulated in Appendices 1 to 8 and supplementary statistics are shown in Tables 1 to 18, which are alongside the relevant text. The statutory reporting requirements are the Railways (Notice of Accidents) Order 1986 (SI No 2187) and the Reporting of Injuries, Diseases and Dangerous Occurrences Regulations 1985 (RIDDOR) (SI No 2023). Wrong side signalling failures (WSF), signals passed at Danger (SPAD) and incidents of severe congestion at stations are reported under administrative arrangements.

Definitions

7   Accidents and failures are divided into four groups:

(a)   *train accidents*, ie accidents to trains and rolling stock;

(b)   *movement accidents*, ie accidents to people caused by the movement of railway vehicles but excluding those involved in train accidents;

(c)   *non-movement accidents*, ie accidents to people on railway premises but not connected with the movement of railway vehicles;

(d) *failures* of rolling stock, track and structures of a type which can cause train accidents.

8   Accidents to people are further subdivided into accidents to:

(a) passengers;

(b) railway staff including contractors' employees;

(c) other persons, including people on business;

(d) occupants of road vehicles (ORV); and

(e) trespassers and suicides.

9   *Significant train accidents* are those that are actually or potentially most dangerous to passengers, whether or not they result in casualties. These include most collisions and all derailments on or affecting passenger lines.

10   *Dangerous occurrences* are a class of incident defined in RIDDOR. They are incidents likely to cause injury and must be reported under RIDDOR if no notifiable injury has actually occurred, unless they are otherwise notifiable under the Railways (Notice of Accidents) Order 1986.

Abbreviations

11   A list of the abbreviations used in this report is given in Appendix 9.

Review of fatal accident statistics

12   Fatal accident figures for 1990 to 1993/94 have been revised following notification of Coroner's findings for inquests which were outstanding at the time the previous statistics were prepared.

Period of report

13   This report is based on incidents during the financial year 1 April 1994 to 31 March 1995.

Chapter 1 ACTIVITIES OF THE RAILWAY INSPECTORATE

Key facts

- The Inspectorate increased its staff from 71 to 85
- The number of Inspecting Officers increased by 51%
- First public inquiry for three years held under the Regulation of Railways Act 1871
- Heavy involvement with Heathrow tunnel collapse and RMT dispute
- First year of the reorganised railway network

Staff

14   Last year's report pointed to the need for the ultimate size of the Inspectorate to be in excess of 80 staff. A strengthening of resources by almost 20% during 1994/95 has largely achieved that aim.

15   The addition of two officers at Assistant Chief Inspecting Officer (ACIO) level in Spring 1994, both from HSE's Field Operations Division, effectively completed the formation of the Inspectorate's enlarged senior management structure. Another internal recruit to a vacant Principal Inspecting Officer (PIO) post underpinned the effort launched during the year to enhance HMRI's information systems. An innovation early in 1995 was the six-month attachment of a Senior Scientific Officer (SSO) to undertake a study of occupational health within the railway industry.

16   The year's most significant staffing development was the establishment of a body of Inspecting Officers (IOs) at Headquarters to support senior staff on the heavily increased work-loads brought about by the changing nature of railway business; in particular, the recent introduction of new safety legislation covering approval of new works, health and safety and the Safety Case requirements. No less than nine IOs were recruited to this new role, most of them from the industry, although two came from the promotion of Higher Professional and Technical Officers who joined the Inspectorate some years ago, a pleasing reflection of the Inspectorate's successful staff development policy. The Inspecting Officer intake also encompassed three staff for the field teams, one of whom was the Inspectorate's first female operational inspector.

17   At 31 March 1995, the total staff figure stood at 85. This comprised the Chief Inspecting Officer, three Deputy Chief Inspecting Officers, six ACIOs, 14 PIOs, 28 IOs (an increase of 51% on the previous year) and an SSO. The administration and secretarial staff at the Inspectorate's Headquarters increased by one to 32.

Principal accident inquiries

18   Major C B Holden, Assistant Chief Inspecting Officer of Railways, was appointed by the Secretary of State for Transport, to conduct an inquiry under section 7 of the Railways Act 1871 into the head on collision between two passenger trains at *Cowden* (RTSZ), Kent. The collision occurred on the single line on the morning of *15 October 1994*. The Public Inquiry into the collision sat for seven days from 5 to 13 December. A further session to hear legal submissions was held at HSE's Rose Court offices on 26 January 1995.

19   Mr N Clarke (PIO) was appointed as an assessor to HM Coroner into the derailment and subsequent passenger train collision at *Ais Gill* (RTNE), Cumbria, on *31 January 1995*. A report into the Inspector's findings will be published, after completion of the inquest.

Approval of new works

20   The Railways and Other Transport Systems (Approval of Works, Plant and Equipment) Regulations 1994 came into force on 5 April 1994. They extended the range of new works and modifications that must be approved. Notably, the Regulations apply to all rolling stock. Also, there is provision for type approval. HSE published a *Guide to the approval of railway works, plant and equipment* in August 1994 (ISBN 0 7176 0741 0, available from HSE Books).

21   The extensive reorganisation of British Railways at the beginning of the year meant that the responsibility for submitting most of the schemes needing approval passed to Railtrack. There was also a considerable change of personnel involved in the process. Consequently, there was some confusion as to:

(a)   which schemes need to be submitted;

(b)   who should submit them;

(c)   what details the Inspectorate requires to make an assessment.

22   The difficulties began to ease following publication of the Guide, but late submission or the need for the Inspectorate to request additional information can still lead to delay in the assessment and approval of schemes. Those concerned are advised to consider carefully the details given in the Guide.

23   A considerable increase in the amount of work being submitted for approval has meant a heavy work-load for those staff involved. This was further exacerbated by the secondment of staff to assist with the review of the collapse of the Heathrow tunnel.

24   There were 62 approvals of new works following inspections, an increase over the previous year of ten (19%), and a further 83 smaller schemes (including bridges) received approval without inspection. The number of schemes is less than the total of 241 reported in the previous year. Under the new Regulations, approval cannot be given subject to condition before any scheme is fully and satisfactorily complete.

25   However, formal letters were sent to confirm that the Inspectorate had no objections to a further 95 schemes, and subject to the works being properly completed they should receive approval in due course.

New works 'Mega' projects

26   During 1994/1995 there was a heightened awareness on the part of the Railway Operators of the implications of the Railways and Other Transport Systems (Approval of Works, Plant and Equipment) Regulations 1994, and the requirement to obtain the approval of the Secretary of State for Transport prior to bringing into use new and altered works.

27   This has led to the Inspectorate having a greater involvement in 'Mega' new works in the conceptual and early stages of the process and an ongoing involvement throughout their development, including approval of the associated temporary and enabling works, to facilitate their progress.

28   The Inspectorate has at present direct involvement with the following projects currently in progress:

■   Channel Tunnel Rail Link;
■   Glasgow Crossrail;
■   Heathrow Express;
■   London Crossrail;
■   LUL Central Line modernisation;
■   LUL East London Line extension;
■   LUL East London Line refurbishment;
■   LUL Jubilee Line extension;
■   LUL Northern Line refurbishment.

29   To deal with the increased work-load, the Inspectorate's resources were increased by the appointment of an additional Inspecting Officer.

30   At the same time the creation of the investigating team for the Heathrow Express Tunnel collapse drew resources from the Inspectorate's 'Mega' new works section, when the approvals work-load was increasing.

31   By their nature these are long-term projects which take years from concept to completion. In many instances they involve Parliamentary process and public enquiries. Since each of the works has its own time-scale, inevitably the current projects are at different stages in their development. In some of them the physical work is underway and some years into the project while others are at the beginning of their life and will involve the Inspectorate for many years to come.

32   During 1994/1995 none of the 'Mega' new works schemes were completed. Inspections carried out during the year were in relation to stage work, temporary work and enabling work.

33   Approvals given during 1994/1995 were similarly in respect of stage work, temporary work and enabling work and where appropriate 'no objection' was made in principle to the design concept.

Level crossing modernisation

34 The reorganisation of the infrastructure management responsibilities of the former British Railways Board, now Railtrack PLC, has not prevented the modernisation of level crossings from proceeding at a steady pace. The equipment at crossings introduced in the mid 1960s, either automatic or manually controlled, is coming to the end of its life and renewal works are required. Many schemes have been dealt with by the Inspectorate and discussions on proposals for others have been ongoing throughout the year.

35 The then British Railways Board undertook to complete by December 1993 replacement of all automatic open crossings remotely monitored (AOCR) and those automatic open crossings locally monitored (AOCL) which failed to meet the criteria specified in the report produced by Professor Stott. At 31 March 1995, all but three AOCLs had been converted and in the case of these three the initial design works were completed. Railtrack is progressing the outstanding works.

36 Numerous site visits combined with consultation meetings were held with county council and local authority representatives. Also, 38 submissions from the railways were processed where major amendments were sought to the protection laid down in statutory orders. This compares with 40 last year. Eighty-six minor amendments were processed compared with 101 last year. Sixty inspections of modernised crossings were carried out during the reporting year, compared with 37 last year. Inspectors of the field operations team have, after training, undertaken an increasing number of these duties.

37 The redrafting of the 1981 Requirements to form a two-part document *Railway safety principles and guidance* for level crossings has been a major task undertaken during the year. The industry also took a very active and supportive role in the preparation of this document. The redrafting was completed by mid-1995 and has since gone out for public consultation.

38 A research project into road user behaviour at level crossings was commissioned from the Transport Research Laboratory (TRL) by HMRI (see Chapter 12).

39 A separate but complementary research project, commissioned by the then BRB, entitled 'Optimising risk reduction at level crossings' was undertaken by Arthur D Little Ltd. A brief summary of the findings can be found in Chapter 12.

The work of field inspectors

40 The disposition and structure of the field teams of inspectors was not fundamentally changed from that created late in the previous year, which took account of the emerging reorganisation of BR. Six Principal Inspecting Officers supervise the work of a total of 20 Inspecting Officers in London and the provinces. At the start of the year there were three IO vacancies, but two were filled by direct entry, leaving one vacancy in the field by the year end.

41 The structure and organisation of the field teams is now aligned to the Railtrack zones and the principal metropolitan railways, while each new 'business', such as Train Operating Companies, emerging from BR is allocated to a lead PIO for that company. Most inspection of minor railways is dealt with similarly, by being allocated to a field inspector appropriate to its location.

42 The period might usefully have been one of consolidation of the new structure and establishing liaison with new management units within the rapidly changing organisation of British Railways. Although this was an important element of field work, other emerging priorities absorbed considerable effort outside the work plan.

43 Early in the year a strong team from various engineering disciplines was assembled to witness 'tests on completion' of a wide range of novel technical features in the Channel Tunnel, while during the summer of 1994 the industrial relations dispute between RMT and Railtrack absorbed a large amount of time and effort in ensuring that where substitute signal operators were used they were competent in terms of the Railways (Safety Critical Work) Regulations 1994. More details of these special projects are given in other chapters.

44 It is part of the operational policy of HMRI to consider in some detail the relevance and effectiveness at working level of

Railtrack's Safety Case, accepted by HMRI in March 1994. The dispute highlighted the need for this and a project to do so was conducted in the last few months of 1994. Detailed criticisms of implementation of the Safety Case, which generally did not have significant effects on safety, were dealt with at Railtrack zone level.

45   In terms of formal enforcement procedures, inspectors issued three Prohibition Notices and 12 Improvement Notices. Three prosecutions arising from breaches of safety legislation were heard in the year, including one case heard in the Crown Court. This involved two defendants, British Railways Board and a contractor, Tilbury Douglas Construction Limited, in relation to an uncontrolled collapse during the demolition of a bridge at St John's Station in 1992.

Railway Industry Advisory Committee (RIAC)

46   RIAC, an advisory committee to the HSC, met on three occasions during the year, under the chairmanship of the Chief Inspecting Officer of Railways. Like other HSC industry-specific advisory committees, its membership comprises representatives of the industry's management and trade unions, but RIAC also now includes members from user groups, namely the Central Rail Users Consultative Committee (CRUCC) and the London Regional Passengers Committee (LRPC).

47   Another innovation this year was that at each meeting a member of HMRI gave a presentation about HMRI's current work in a particular area. In addition to regular presentations by the Occupational Health Working Group, HSE technical staff described the work in hand to review occupational health issues in the railway sector and identify priorities for action.

48   Passenger group representatives (CRUCC and LRPC) particularly welcomed a paper and report on the reduction in falls from trains in motion and details of the further steps being taken for better security of train doors in the future. A summary was made available to the user representative groups for public information.

49   A recurring topic was the review of railway safety legislation and the development of relevant guidance or Approved Codes of Practice (ACOPs) in support of legislation. Of particular note, the work of a special sub-committee of RIAC proved invaluable in assisting HSE to further the preparation of an ACOP in support of the Railways (Safety Critical Work) Regulations 1994.

50   The guidance on prevention of risk to workers on the track, prepared by the Track Safety Working Group (TSWG) was approved by RIAC and the HSC, and published in May 1995. The TSWG did not meet during 1994/95 but will probably do so again, particularly to review the effect of a radical revision of track safety rules on the Railtrack infrastructure, which took place in April 1995.

Assistance to other railways

51   An Assistant Chief Inspecting Officer is responsible for providing guidance on railway safety matters to the Department of Environment for Northern Ireland. The main work this year concerned the construction of the cross-harbour rail link over the River Lagan which was built in conjunction with the parallel road link. Both bridges and links were formally opened by HM the Queen on 9 March 1995. The whole of the railway project consisted of closing York Street Station and building a new Central Servicing Depot on its site, and constructing a new station to replace it at Yorkgate and the new single link which now connects the Larne line to the main Belfast to Dublin line. Preliminary work is being undertaken on two other major projects: reinstatement of the line between Antrim and Bleach Green and the upgrading of the cross-border main line. The latter also entails the purchase of new locomotives and rolling stock. The same Inspecting Officer is also involved in the advice to the Republic of Ireland on the proposed Dublin LRT system. One of the Deputy Chief Inspecting Officers continues to give advice to the Hong Kong Government on rail projects, in particular the Lantau Airport Rail Link.

Automatic train protection (ATP)

52   Automatic train protection (ATP) is the generic name given to systems which prevent trains from making unsafe movements by automatically applying the brakes if the driver fails to respond correctly to a signal. Some systems of ATP also prevent drivers from exceeding speed limits or approaching buffer stops at too high a speed.

53 A number of railways in Great Britain are equipped with ATP systems. London Underground has for many years had a system known as the 'train stop' fitted to its entire network. In this system if a train passes a signal at Danger, its brakes are applied when a lever under the train is struck by a mechanical arm which is raised at the track side; similar protection is provided on Glasgow Underground. A more modern form, with inductive transmission replacing the contact arms, is provided on the mass-transit systems of Tyne and Wear Metro, and Manchester Metrolink, while the automatic train control systems of the Docklands Light Railway incorporate a sophisticated form of ATP. All trains using the Channel Tunnel are equipped with an ATP system which ensures adherence to signals and speed restrictions on Eurotunnel's infrastructure.

54 Human error is frequently identified as a cause of industrial accidents, and railway accidents are no exception. Many protective systems, such as signal interlocking, have been introduced in the past to minimise the scope for railway accidents caused by human error, but the task of train driving remains relatively unprotected by such systems. As a result driver error, especially in the case of signals passed at Danger (SPAD), has continued to be a major cause of train accidents. Public inquiries into a number of serious accidents, for example to collisions at Bellegrove, Purley, and Newton Junction, and the buffer stop collision at Cannon Street, have produced recommendations that ATP should be fitted on the BR network. Although the accident at Clapham in 1988, in which 35 people died, was not preventable by ATP, the public inquiry held by Sir Anthony Hidden recommended that it should be installed across the network. British Rail undertook to examine and pilot such a system.

55 BR developed a specification for an ATP system based on those currently being installed in Europe which would prevent accidents caused by trains overspeeding or passing signals at Danger. Two systems were adopted for pilot schemes, one on the Great Western route between London (Paddington) and Bristol Parkway and the other on the Chiltern Lines from London (Marylebone) Station. Both schemes proved to be technically successful, but the emerging costs caused BR to make an in-depth review of the benefits and costs which would arise if the piloted ATP systems were to be widely fitted on the rail network.

56 In March 1994, BR submitted a report to the Secretary of State for Transport in which they described the results of their study into the network-wide fitment of ATP, based on a cost benefit appraisal of national application of the systems used in the pilot schemes. The Secretary of State asked the HSC for advice on several issues relating to the report, principally on the main conclusion by BR that ATP as piloted was too expensive to be generally adopted on the existing rail network and did not represent good value for money. The HSC asked HSE and HMRI to consider the BR report and examine its conclusions.

57 In their response, the HSC accepted the BR report as being basically sound and hence supported the conclusion that, as piloted, it was not reasonably practicable. But the Commission advised that a system providing the functions of ATP should be adopted as standard on new high-speed lines, including the Channel Tunnel Rail Link. The Commission also advised that full consideration should be given to installing ATP functions within future major resignalling works, such as modernisation of the West Coast Main Line, where the provision of such systems or other risk reduction measures was reasonably practicable.

58 The HSC also said that action needed to be taken to reduce the risks associated with SPAD, overspeeding and buffer stop collisions, and that they had requested HSE (HMRI) to discuss with Railtrack and BR means for reducing these risks. The Secretary of State accepted the advice given by HSC. The HSC's report to the Secretary of State and his response and announcement in Parliament are reproduced in Appendix 12.

59 BR and Railtrack have in hand a number of measures to reduce the risks that would have been controlled by ATP. BR have adopted a number of initiatives to improve drivers' performance by better selection, training and supervision, together with campaigns to raise drivers' awareness of the risks of SPAD. Railtrack and BR will be piloting a passive device to be fitted in the cab for the driver to use as a reminder when stopped at a red signal to reduce the probability of starting against it. This trial is due for completion in 1995. Railtrack will also pilot an enhanced version of the present automatic warning system (AWS) which will provide some of the functions of ATP at a much reduced cost and this trial is due for completion by the end of 1996.

60   In the longer term, Railtrack is considering the modernisation of the West Coast Main Line using a train control system based on continuous information transmission and cab signalling which would inherently include the functions of ATP. If successful, this technology would be adopted for other major modernisation schemes, and could ultimately become the standard form of train control for much of the Railtrack network.

61   The existing ATP pilot installations will remain in service, and may even be extended to include the Heathrow rail link.

62   In addition to human error, some SPADs and buffer stop collisions result from braking and wheel/rail adhesion difficulties. BR and Railtrack are pursuing a wide range of initiatives to improve braking performance even under conditions of poor adhesion.

63   HMRI will be closely monitoring the progress of all of these risk reduction initiatives and will be reporting on progress to the HSC.

The study of the collapse of a tunnel at Heathrow

64   On 21 October 1994 there was a partial collapse of tunnels under construction for the Heathrow Express railway line at the Central Terminal Area (CTA) at Heathrow Airport which resulted in the formation of a large surface crater and substantial damage to an adjacent building. The tunnels were being constructed using the New Austrian Tunnelling Method (NATM). One of the tunnels that collapsed extended beneath the Piccadilly Line just to the west of the CTA station.

65   Although the collapse was some distance from the Piccadilly Line, the line was immediately closed by LUL as a precautionary measure. Following a thorough survey of Piccadilly Line tunnels at CTA and discussions between the Inspectorate, and LUL, the Piccadilly Line reopened from Hatton Cross to Heathrow CTA station using the double track alignment which existed prior to the completion of the Piccadilly Line Loop and which had been retained. The CTA station was outside the possible zone of influence of any further collapse. Immediate measures were put in hand to fill the intact sections of tunnel with concrete to prevent any further collapse.

66   The Piccadilly Line loops under Heathrow Airport and passes above further works at Heathrow Terminal 4 (T4) which had already been constructed using NATM. Services to T4 only resumed once substantial temporary strengthening works had been completed in the NATM tunnels at T4 and the tunnels at CTA had been completely filled with concrete.

67   Following the collapse, all NATM work in the United Kingdom was voluntarily suspended including tunnelling on parts of the Heathrow Express Railway and London Underground's Jubilee Line extension. HSE set up a Project Board to oversee its investigation into the causes of the collapse, to review the further use of NATM and to endorse the restart of any works using NATM, the Chief Inspecting Officer of Railways being a member of this Board. In December 1994 the Jubilee Line extension project team submitted proposals to resume tunnelling work using NATM. HSE reviewed these proposals and agreed additional measures including substantial redesign, improvement in management arrangements and improved provisions to deal with any possible emergencies, following which HSE indicated, on 13 January 1995, that it had no objection to the work proceeding on 5.35 m diameter running tunnels only.

68   Further submissions were received for the resumption of works on Waterloo and London Bridge stations, on the Jubilee Line extension and for works at T4 on Heathrow Express, and are the subject of ongoing discussion. Major works will be required to retrieve the situation on Heathrow Express at CTA and to allow the completion of the CTA station. The suspension of works and the subsequent reviews of design, management and emergency arrangements will cause delays in the completion of both the Heathrow Express Railway and the Jubilee Line extension.

RMT dispute 1994

69   Industrial action by signalling staff members of the RMT Union, consisting of a series of one- and two-day strikes, began on 15 June 1994. Some trains were operated on each strike day, facilitated by signalmen who were not RMT members and the substitution of supervisors or managers for signal operators on strike. There were 23 strike days, the last being on 23 September 1994.

70   Railtrack has a duty to ensure that staff operating the equipment at signal-boxes and signalling centres are competent to do so, in accordance with the Health and Safety at Work etc Act 1974 (HSW Act) and, more specifically, the Railways (Safety Critical Work) Regulations 1994 (RSCW). The RSCW Regulations require employers to ensure that employees involved in safety critical work are competent to carry out their jobs and do not work such hours as might cause fatigue leading to danger. No specific hours are laid down by statute.

71   On every strike day, HMRI inspectors visited some of the signal-boxes that were open. They checked the way in which competence had been assessed and the hours worked, questioned the stand-in signalmen about their knowledge and experience and assessed their competence. As Railtrack increased the intensity of strike day services, HMRI insisted that commensurate efforts were made to ensure that levels of competence were maintained.

72   Over 100 specific allegations of incompetence about incidents on strike days were made to HMRI and these were investigated on a priority basis according to the implications for safety. The majority had no significant safety implications. Overall, HMRI were satisfied that Railtrack adequately managed the issue of competence of stand-in signalmen.

Figure 1   Railway fatalities

Number of fatal injuries

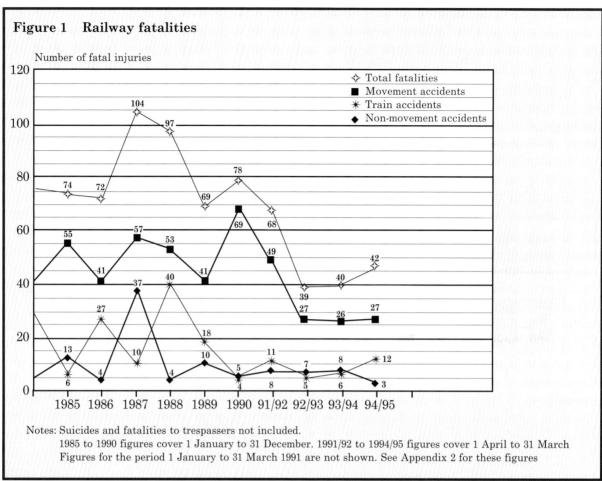

Notes: Suicides and fatalities to trespassers not included.
1985 to 1990 figures cover 1 January to 31 December. 1991/92 to 1994/95 figures cover 1 April to 31 March
Figures for the period 1 January to 31 March 1991 are not shown. See Appendix 2 for these figures

Figure 2   Causes of train accidents

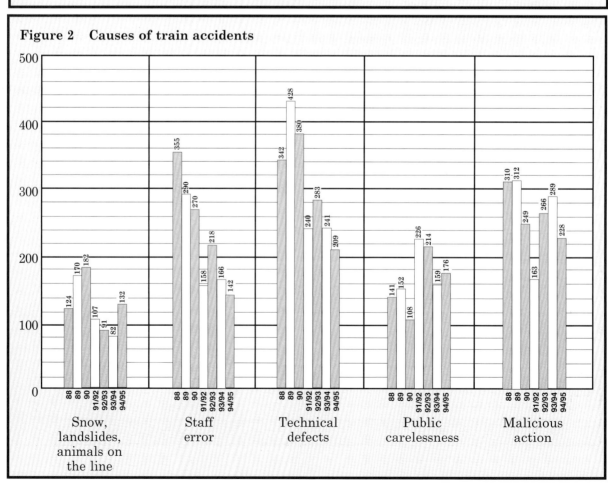

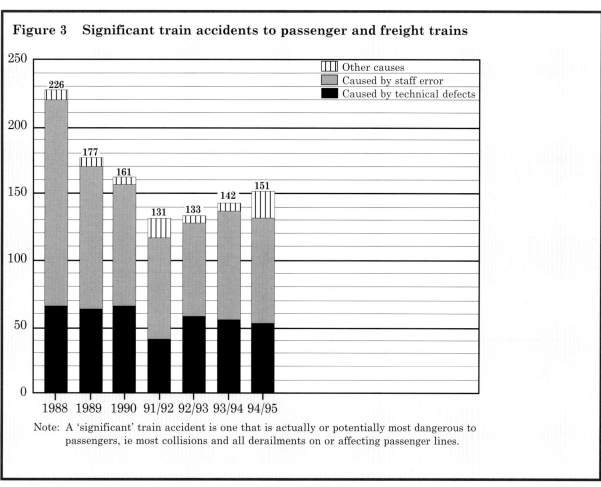

Figure 3   Significant train accidents to passenger and freight trains

Legend:
- Other causes
- Caused by staff error
- Caused by technical defects

Note: A 'significant' train accident is one that is actually or potentially most dangerous to passengers, ie most collisions and all derailments on or affecting passenger lines.

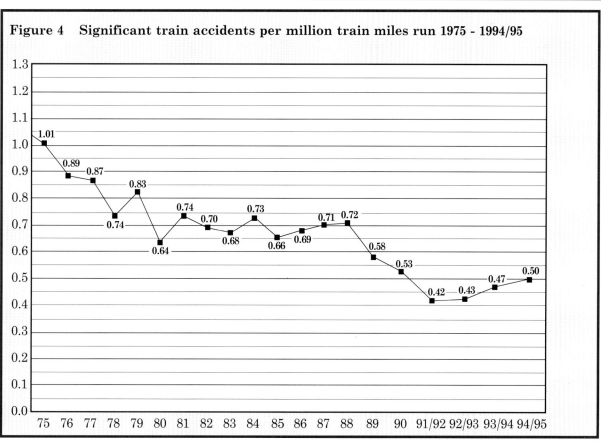

Figure 4   Significant train accidents per million train miles run 1975 - 1994/95

Chapter 2 ACCIDENTS TO PASSENGERS, STAFF AND OTHERS

Key facts

■ A total of 42 passengers, staff and other persons killed, an increase of two on last year's figures

■ Seventeen passengers killed, an increase of one on last year

■ Nine railway staff killed, an increase of one on last year

■ Sixteen other persons killed, the same as last year

■ Three passengers killed in a train collision or derailment

■ Five railway staff killed in a train collision or derailment

■ Six passengers killed falling from carriages during running between stations, two less than previous year, continuing less than half rate of earlier years

■ Five passengers killed falling from slam doors

Summary

73   During 1994/95, excluding trespassers and suicides, 42 people died in accidents on the railways. This is an increase of two on the previous year. Of concern is the number of passenger and staff fatalities in train accidents. Three passengers were killed, the first passenger train accident fatalities for two years. Five railway staff lost their lives in train accidents. The total number of people killed in train accidents doubled from six the previous year to 12 but such small total numbers within the total scope of operation does not represent a statistically significant trend. This chapter discusses the accident figures in Appendices 1 to 8, looks at accident rates and notable comparisons with last year, and describes some of the more serious accidents not dealt with elsewhere in the report. Except where otherwise specified, the term 'railways' includes tramways, metropolitan railways and minor railways.

Accident rates

74   Table 1 sets out fatal, major and minor injury rates since 1989 for train accidents, movement accidents and non-movement accidents. A definition of these categories is given in the Introduction in paragraphs 7 to 10. The figures are derived from operating statistics obtained from railway operators collated in Appendix 1, and the analysis of fatal, major and minor injuries listed in Appendix 2. (Table 1 is repeated after Appendix 2 for comparison.)

75   Train and movement accidents are related to billions of passenger miles. Non-movement accidents are shown per billion passenger journeys as that figure relates more closely to the use of stations.

Table 1   Death or injury rate: passengers

Year	Train accidents *per billion passenger miles*			Movement accidents *per billion passenger miles*			Non-movement accidents *per billion passenger journeys*		
	Killed	Major	Minor	Killed	Major	Minor	Killed	Major	Minor
1989	0.24	1.58	11.03	1.01	3.93	105.40	1.25	82.55	2687
1990	-	0.53	5.88	1.43	4.37	104.10	1.29	67.31	2294
1991/92	0.08	0.75	12.01	1.16	3.03	90.65	0.63	63.64	2091
1992/93	-	0.13	2.67	0.68	3.35	98.93	1.29	100.26	2395
1993/94	-	0.22	5.67	0.62	1.80	95.37	1.30	103.05	2793
1994/95	0.14	0.50	8.17	0.55	2.65	98.41	1.26	85.28	2685

Fatal accidents

76   During the year, the Inspectorate reviewed the previous years' fatal accident figures, and adjusted them based on the notification of Coroner's findings for inquests that were outstanding at the time the previous figures were produced.

77   Appendix 2 shows that of the 42 fatal casualties, 17 were passengers, nine were railway or contractors' employees and 16 were other members of the public. This is very close to the 16, eight and 16 respectively the previous year. Unfortunately, train accidents accounted for 12 of the fatalities, double the figure for 1993/94, including three passengers and five railway staff. Movement accidents accounted for 27 deaths, of which 12 were passengers, three railway staff and 12 other persons. The total number of people killed in non-movement accidents, three, was the lowest on record.

78   Of the total 16 people killed in the category 'Other persons', three were occupants of road vehicles killed at level crossings and ten were pedestrians struck by trains at level crossings, further details of which are given in Chapter 4. A car driver was killed and her passenger received serious injuries when the car fell from a motorway onto the running line below into the path of an oncoming train. Both other accidents in this category occurred on Blackpool Transport, in separate incidents, when pedestrians were struck and killed attempting to cross the tramway.

Train accidents

79   Three passengers were killed, two in a passenger train collision and one as a result of a derailment caused by vandals placing an obstruction on the line. These were the first passenger fatalities in train accidents since the train collision at *Newton* (RTSc), Strathclyde on *10 April 1991*. This long interval is itself a powerful testimony to the inherent safety of rail travel. Major injuries to passengers rose from five to 11 and minor injuries increased by 50 from 129 to 179. Five railway staff were killed in this category,

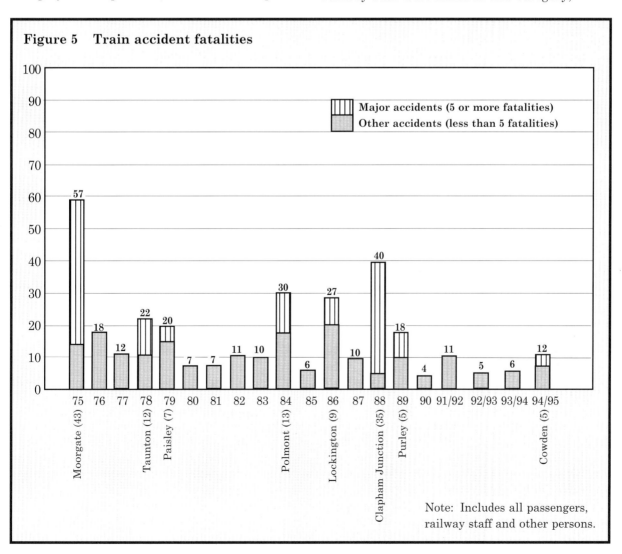

Figure 5   Train accident fatalities

Major accidents (5 or more fatalities)
Other accidents (less than 5 fatalities)

Note: Includes all passengers, railway staff and other persons.

Table 2   Train accident fatalities 1975 - 1994/95 by category

Year	Passengers	Railway staff	Other persons	Total
1975	47	7	3	57
1976	-	8	10	18
1977	-	3	9	12
1978	13	3	6	22
1979	8	8	4	20
1980	-	4	3	7
1981	4	1	2	7
1982	-	8	3	11
1983	2	1	7	10
1984	18	6	6	30
1985	-	-	6	6
1986	8	5	14	27
1987	3	1	6	10
1988	34	2	4	40
1989	6	6	6	18
1990	-	1	3	4
1991	2	-	1	3
1991/92	2	2	7	11
1992/93	-	1	4	5
1993/94	-	-	6	6
1994/95	3	5	4	12
Total	150	72	114	336

Note: The figures for 1991 cover the period 1 January 1991 - 31 March 1991

four in collisions and one in a derailment. Again this was a backward step in the trend of decreasing fatalities in train accidents. Four people, all occupants of road vehicles, were killed when trains struck their vehicles, a reduction of two from the previous year.

80   While the number of injuries in train accidents increased, the actual number of train accidents reduced by 70 (7%). Tram accidents increased by seven from 44 to 51 of which the majority were derailments and running into obstructions.

81   Significant train accidents rose by nine from 142 to 151, however the number of significant collisions actually fell from 55 in 1993/94 to 44, with collisions at buffer stops totalling 21, a reduction of ten. Significant derailments rose by 23 from 87 to 107.

82   Figure 5 illustrates the number of train accident fatalities for the period 1975 to 1994/95, and graphically shows the increase recorded this year. A further breakdown listing fatalities by category is shown in Table 2.

83   The total number of casualties in train accidents are detailed in Appendix 5. These are summarised in Table 3.

Table 3   Casualties in train accidents

1993/94	Fatal	Major	Minor	Total
Passengers	-	5	129	134
Staff	-	4	91	95
Other persons	6	2	15	23
Total	6	11	235	252

1994/95	Fatal	Major	Minor	Total
Passengers	3	11	179	193
Staff	5	8	75	88
Other persons	4	5	18	27
Total	12	24	272	308

Movement accidents

84 Movement accidents include people struck by trains, falling out of trains, and injured when boarding or alighting. In 1994/95, 12 passengers, two less than the previous year's record low, and three employees were killed. Twelve other persons were killed, an increase of three, of which ten occurred at level crossings.

85 Of the 12 passengers killed, six fell out of carriages between stations, five of whom fell from slam doors and one through a window. This is two less than the previous year, and again is confirmation that following publication of HSE's report into passenger falls from train doors, raising standards and public awareness has improved the accident rate. Although much progress has been made by the railway, the Inspectorate has continued to monitor maintenance standards of doors and locks, and technical modifications. All Intercity trains now have a centralised door locking system fitted, operated by the guard, who normally will only free the doors to be opened when stationary at the platform.

86 Three passengers died through falling or jumping off platforms into the path of moving trains; all three occurred on LUL. Two other fatalities on LUL fall into the category of entering/alighting from trains and crossing the lines. Full details of these are in Chapter 8.

87 The danger of leaning out of windows while the train is in motion was emphasised with a tragic accident north of *Pulborough Station* (RTSZ), West Sussex. A male passenger suffered fatal head injuries when he leaned out of the window and struck his head on a bridge support. In a similar accident between *Portsmouth Harbour* and *Woking* (RTSW) a male passenger received severe head injuries when he struck his head against a lineside object.

88 Major and minor injuries in movement accidents showed a slight increase on the previous year's figures. There have been more reported cases of drivers or guards suffering from shock, usually when a person is struck on the line or jumps in front of the train.

Non-movement accidents

89 Only three fatalities were recorded in this category, the lowest on record. At *St Neots Station* (WAGN), Cambridgeshire, an elderly male passenger slipped on the stairs of the station and died from his injuries. The stairs were in a satisfactory state of repair and no cause of the fall could be found. At *Finchley Road and Frognall Station* (RTEA), North West London, a 25-year-old man, while waiting for his train, fell off the platform and came into contact with the live rail. A contractor's employee working for LUL was electrocuted when he fell onto the live rails (see Chapter 8 for details).

90 Major and minor injuries both decreased. As in previous years the majority of passenger accidents in this category are due to slips, trips and falls, and injuries sustained in using steps and escalators at stations.

The dangers of trespassing: new fencing material had been stacked against the railway boundary wall. A 15-year-old youth climbed onto the stack and threw metallic audio tape onto the OLE - he received 30% burns

Trespassers and suicides

91 Appendix 8 gives a breakdown of casualties resulting from trespass and suicide on the railway. Six children under the age of 16 were killed trespassing on railway property, a reduction of one on the previous year. Four were killed by being struck by trains, one electrocuted by the conductor rail and one falling while playing on an escalator at a station.

92   At *Battersea Park Station* (RTSZ), Greater London, a 13-year-old boy was showing off to his younger brother. As the train left the station, the deceased got onto the footboard at the doorway, grabbed the handrail and travelled on the outside of the train. He then slipped off the footboard and fell under the wheels of the EMU.

93   A nine-year-old boy who was partially deaf, trespassed on the railway and was struck and killed by a passenger train at *Goole* (RTNE), Humberside. A tragic accident at an unmanned station occurred at *East Dulwich* (RTSZ), Greater London, where a nine-year-old girl who was playing with friends, initially on the platform and later on the track came into contact with the conductor. One of the deceased's friends received burns to her hands when she tried to help the deceased off the rail. Following this accident, Network SouthCentral launched a publicity campaign to highlight the dangers of children playing on electrified lines and a copy of their poster appears below. In addition, the Inspectorate have commissioned research into the problem of child trespass generally, and at unmanned stations in particular.

Poster highlighting the dangers of child trespass and the danger from electrified lines

94   At *St James* (T&W), Northumberland, a nine-year-old boy fell over 40 feet from the side of an escalator while playing on it. At *Newington* (RTSZ), Kent, a 12-year-old boy under the impression that a gang of boys were chasing him ran into the path of an EMU. In a similar incident at *Barrhead* (RTSc), Strathclyde, a 14-year-old youth was fleeing from a gang fight when he ran into the path of an express passenger train. The Inspectorate continues to encourage the commendable efforts made by the operators, police and schools to warn children of the dangers the railways hold.

95   Trespass on the railways is not just confined to children. Between *Benfleet* and *Leigh-on-Sea* (RTE), Essex, a twenty-one-year-old male under the influence of alcohol climbed onto the outside of a train in an attempt to 'train surf' and fell to his death. Two male students in their early 20s had been out drinking; on their way home they trespassed onto railway sidings at *Preston* (RTWC) Lancashire, and decided to climb on top of empty coaching stock. In doing so one of the men came into contact with the overhead wires (OLE) and received 80% burns which proved fatal. His friend tried to save him, but received minor burns and a fractured leg when he fell from the unit. Alcohol again was a contributory factor in the death of two brothers killed while attempting to take a short cut home, crossing the lines at *Leagrave* (RTMZ), Bedfordshire, when they were struck by a high-speed passenger train.

96   The increase in members of the public using mobile telephones may have been a contributory factor in the death of an off duty railway worker at *Clapham* (RTSZ), Greater London. Despite being aware of the dangers of crossing the lines, the deceased went onto the track, possibly to obtain better reception when making a call from his mobile phone. He was struck and killed by a passenger train.

97   All these accidents could have been avoided if the people had obeyed the safety warnings not to trespass onto areas where they had no right to be.

Chapter 3 TRAIN ACCIDENTS

Key facts

- Total reported train accidents 70 fewer at 907
- Derailments up 36 at 149
- Significant train accidents on BR/RT down eight to 110
- Significant train accidents on all railways up nine to 151
- Five people killed in head-on collision at Cowden
- Railway guard killed in collision at Ais Gill
- Driver and passenger killed in derailment at Branchton due to vandalism

Summary

98   The total of reported train accidents in 1994/95 was 907, significantly fewer than in the previous year. Appendix 3 analyses the figures and shows that, although the total is less, there are several areas in which the trend is reversed. Appendix 3 also deals with failures (see Chapter 6) and fires (see Chapter 5). Accidents at level crossings are considered in detail in Chapter 4.

Collisions

99   Ten fewer collisions occurred in 1994/95 than in the previous year. (This has been brought about largely by looking more stringently at the 'damage to train' criterion in the category of trains striking buffer stops in the Railways (Notice of Accidents) Order 1986, and the exclusion of reports of incidents where such damage was not incurred.)

Collisions between passenger trains

100   Two DEMU passenger trains collided head-on just south of *Cowden Station* (RTSZ), Kent, shortly after 08.00 on the foggy morning of Saturday, *15 October 1994.* Two passengers, the two drivers and a guard were killed after the Up train passed the signal at Danger leading from the double line at Ashurst to the single line section. As noted in paragraph 18, a public inquiry into this accident was held and a detailed report has been published.

Table 4   Total number of significant train accidents on all railways 1989 - 1994/95

	1989	1990	1991/92	1992/93	1993/94	Five year average	1994/95
Collisions involving passenger trains	23	14	13	7	14	14	18
Trains running into the buffers at stations	55	41	31	25	31	37	21
Derailments of passenger trains	32	26	23	30	29	28	28
Collisions and derailments of freight trains on passenger lines	67	80	64	71	68	70	84
Total	177	161	131	133	142	149	151

Table 4A   Total number of significant train accidents 1989 - 1994/95 (BR/Railtrack only)

	1989	1990	1991/92	1992/93	1993/94	Five year average	1994/95
Collisions involving passenger trains	17	14	10	6	13	12	14
Trains running into the buffers at stations	54	41	28	23	31	35	20
Derailments of passenger trains	23	23	13	11	11	16	9
Collisions and derailments of freight trains on passenger lines	61	77	63	62	63	65	67
Total	155	155	114	102	118	129	110

101 More than usually bleak winter weather was being experienced on the Settle and Carlisle Line on *31 January 1995* as the 16.26 Carlisle to Leeds train was terminated at Blea Moor, high in the Pennines, and ordered back to Carlisle, when the line ahead of it was closed because of flooding in a tunnel. After crossing to the Down line, the train was heading north when it ran into a landslip near *Ais Gill* (RTNE), Cumbria, and was derailed, foul of the Up line. Fearing the approach of the next train in the Up direction, the 17.45 Carlisle to Leeds, which was approaching their location, the injured driver called on his National Railway Network (NRN) radio to inform the Traffic Controller of the emergency and to request other trains to be stopped. Crewe Control answered and there followed a somewhat confusing exchange. It appears that the train crew of the derailed train believed that Crewe Control would stop other traffic, for neither man took the urgent and fundamental action of protecting the obstruction from the approach of another train by flag or lamp and detonators. The guard of the disabled train was assisting passengers from the front to the rear coach when the second train collided with the first, killing the guard and injuring some 21 passengers and three staff. Five people were reported to have been detained in hospital.

The role of train radio

102 This was the second accident in the year which provoked discussion regarding train radio systems. At Oxted Signal-box, on *15 October 1994*, the signalman was aware of the possibility of a collision between two passenger trains south of *Cowden* (RTSZ), Kent, when his signalling equipment warned him of the situation, but he was unable to prevent it. The Inspector appointed to conduct the public inquiry into the accident concluded that had cab secure radio (CSR) been available, providing secure communication between the signal-box and train driver, this accident could have been prevented. In the Ais Gill accident, both trains were equipped with NRN open net cab to shore radio. When the driver called to report the emergency, the message was received in the radio control centre at Crewe, Cheshire, which was appropriate to the radio signal that his equipment could propagate. However, railway operating control for the traffic on this line was in Leeds, West Yorkshire. The amount of time from the first accident (derailment caused by running into a landslip) to the second train colliding with the first, was some 7 to 8 minutes. Before this time had elapsed, the second train had passed the last signal controlling its progress towards the

Table 5   Train accident inquiries started in 1994/95

Date	Accident	Inquiry sessions
15 October 1994	Head-on collision between two passenger trains on single line at Cowden (RTSZ)	5 to 9 December 1994 12 to 13 December 1994 26 January 1995

Table 6   Significant collisions

Year	Total	Between passenger trains	Between passenger and other trains	Between non-passenger trains	With buffer stops
1989	85	12	11	7	55
1990	59	4	10	4	41
1991/92	52	10	3	8	31
1992/93	35	6	1	3	25
1993/94	55	9	5	10	31
Average 1989 to 1993/94	57	8	6	6	37
1994/95	44	7	11	5	21

The result of the collision between two passenger trains at Cowden on 15 October 1994. The underframe of the overturned leading coach of the Down train is on the left and the superstructureless frame from the Up train is on the right

PHOTOGRAPH COURTESY OF KENT CONSTABULARY

obstruction and Crewe Control had been unable to pass the urgent message to either the train or to Leeds Control in time to prevent the collision.

Collisions between passenger trains and freight trains or light locomotives

103 The 09.43 Newquay to Edinburgh high-speed train (HST) was running through the outskirts of Edinburgh, Lothian, on *13 August 1994*, when it was struck, head-on at *Abbeyhill Junction* (RTSc) by light locomotive 37 113 which was running away wrong line from Edinburgh Waverley Station. Fortunately, the HST was travelling very slowly at the time of the collision, when the locomotive struck it at about 25 mile/h. The runaway had arrived in Waverley Station, Platform 10, some 13 minutes late at about 18.38, after working the 14.30 Inverness to Edinburgh passenger train. The driver then had only seven minutes in which to secure his train and proceed to Platform 18, take over another train, check that it was in order, and depart at 18.45. At about 20.30, the locomotive was seen to move slowly out of Platform 10 and gather speed on the falling gradient to Abbeyhill Junction, where it collided with the HST. The driver and 44 of the 153 passengers were conveyed to hospital for treatment. Four people, including the driver, were seriously injured. The primary cause of the accident was the locomotive from Inverness being left without handbrakes applied. It was subsequently uncoupled from its coaches and gradually the air brake leaked off, enabling it to move off down the gradient

to Abbeyhill Junction under the force of gravity.

104 Remarkably, only eight passengers and six crew suffered minor injury and shock in another serious runaway which occurred on *9 April 1994*, on the 1 in 70 gradient falling between *Dormans* and *Lingfield Stations* (RTSZ), Surrey. In this case, a four-coach electric multiple unit (EMU) had failed just short of Dormans Station, on the Down line. It was decided to use the following train, the 07.54 London Victoria to East Grinstead, a similar EMU, to assist the failed unit forward to East Grinstead, a routine operation. The assisting train stopped behind the failed one and the crew of the former alighted to determine the nature of the failure and decide on a course of action. The problem concerned traction current and the two drivers were attending to a defective contact shoe, which had previously been isolated, when the insulating 'paddle' between the shoe and the live rail was removed, dropping the shoe back onto the rail and causing the traction current from Dormans Power Sub-station to 'blow out'. The drivers set about isolating the shoe again while the guards walked to Dormans Sub-station to explain what was happening and what their plans were. During this time the drivers became aware of the assisting train rolling away backwards down the steep gradient, and its driver ran after it, tripping and falling as the train moved out of reach, gathering speed. Soon, the loud noise of impact was heard in the distance as the train, having run some 1.2 km, collided with a

Collision at Wanstead Park on 18 February 1995.
Damage to the driver's cab of the DMU passenger train (left). Damage to the Freightliner train (right)
PHOTOGRAPHS COURTESY OF BRITISH TRANSPORT POLICE

76-tonne Class 33 locomotive, which was standing at Lingfield Station, propelling it about 391 m to the rear.

105 Investigation established that, when the driver stopped the assisting train behind the one that had failed, he did not immobilise it correctly. It took only some five to ten minutes for the air brake to leak off sufficiently to allow the train to move on the 1 in 70 gradient.

106 Several other runaways, mostly works trains or vehicles and none as dangerous as the previous two examples, have occurred and almost invariably the cause has been the failure of the train crew to secure trains or vehicles properly. The correct procedures are entirely adequate when conscientiously applied but all too often lives are put at risk and damage is caused by 'short cuts' being taken, frequently for reasons of speed. The Inspectorate has agreed with the Operators that railway staff be urgently reminded of the appropriate rules and procedures through briefing and training as necessary.

107 On Saturday, *18 February 1995*, the 12.30 Barking to Gospel Oak 2-car DMU passenger train departed from Woodgrange Park Station without authority against a signal at Danger.

About 200 yards short of *Wanstead Park Station* (RTEA), Greater London, it collided with the rear of the 13.35 Ripple Lane to Southampton Freightliner train which was standing at a Red signal. Two passengers and the guard were reported to have suffered serious injury while 26 passengers and the two drivers had only minor injury or shock. There were about 63 passengers on the train. The signalman at Woodgrange Park witnessed the passenger train departing against the signal but was unable to do anything to prevent it. After the collision, the driver admitted that the guard had given the 'right away' signal and that he had then started the train without checking the aspect of the signal.

108 Two Class 303 EMU, total six cars, forming an empty coaching stock (ECS) train from Lanark to Motherwell passed the Holytown Junction Signal at Danger, ran through the trailing points at the junction, and collided with the rear of the 17.52 Edinburgh via Shotts to Glasgow Class 156 DMU passenger train which had just arrived at *Holytown Station* (RTSc), Strathclyde, at about 21.05 on *1 November 1994*. Testing of the signalling and the train brakes showed no fault in either. British Railways Scientific Services took rail head swabs to determine whether leaf mulch contamination was

present and were able to confirm that it was. It was established that, having run through this mulch, the driver's braking technique was at fault but that there were also shortcomings in the Operator's braking instructions to drivers. The latter were revised forthwith in Scotland, following the Inspectorate's investigation of this accident, with national amendment to follow where necessary. Identification of low adhesion areas and development of means of dealing with the hazards were further recommendations.

Collisions between freight trains, light locomotives or other moving vehicles

109 A failed empty DMU was being recovered from the Up Loop at *Belford* (RTEC), Northumberland, on *1 April 1994*. The driver of the assisting DMU which had been coupled to the front of the failure and was standing in advance of the starting signal, having discussed the situation with the signalman, then wrongly concluded that the main line signal he saw cleared and the level crossing barriers being lowered were for his train. Approaching the trailing connection with the Up Main, he noticed that the points were lying Main to Main and realised his mistake. He reversed his train and the collision that occurred with two Class 37 diesel locomotives running 'light' was only a glancing blow, causing superficial damage to locomotive 37 152 and DMU 158 771. Following this accident, the Inspectorate reopened with Railtrack the ongoing discussion of flank protection in circumstances such as these.

110 The Inspectorate has been concerned by certain incidents involving permanent way machinery of various types being operated both on the running line going to, or coming from engineers' possessions, and within the possessions. A lack of planning and discipline has been detected in certain cases and discussions have taken place with the engineers concerned.

111 On *24 April 1994*, at the conclusion of work in a possession of the line, at *Longniddry* (RTSc), Lothian, a ballast regulator moved up to the signal controlling exit from the possession and stopped in obedience to its Red aspect and to ask permission of the Edinburgh signalman to leave the possession. Two other machines, coupled together, were following the first one but did not stop when it did. The operator of the first machine was injured in the collision and normal working could not be resumed for nearly five hours.

The destruction caused by the buffer stop collision at Slough on 2 November 1994
PHOTOGRAPH COURTESY OF BRITISH TRANSPORT POLICE

112 No personal injury was suffered in the collision between two road/rail vehicles proceeding to their place of work on the line between *Kildwick* and *Steeton* (RTEC), West Yorkshire on the night of *6 March 1995*. One vehicle stopped and the other collided with it at about 15 mile/h.

Collisions between trains and buffer stops

113 There were ten fewer buffer stop collisions in 1994/95 than in the previous year. Of the 21 reported, that which caused the most concern was the accident which befell 3-car DMU 165 102, a 'Thames Turbo' train built in 1992. Working the 19.41 Paddington to Slough service on Wednesday, *2 November 1994*, stopping at all stations except Acton Main Line, it was running close to scheduled time, through light rain, as it approached *Slough* (RTGW), Berkshire, on its last $2^1/_4$ miles from Langley. The driver started braking about 900 m from his destination when his train was travelling at 56 to 57 mile/h. It was therefore surprising that the train was still travelling at some 25 mile/h when it struck the buffers of No 6 Bay and the leading coach mounted the platform with the centre coach straddling the buffer stop. That nobody on-board the train was injured is remarkable, and that so little apparent structural damage was done to the vehicles says much for the sturdy design and construction of these units.

Derailment of the Kings Cross to Glasgow parcels train at Morpeth on 27 June 1994

114 The on-board data recorders fitted to these new trains assisted the investigation and showed that wheelslide protection (WSP - the automatic, rapid and continued release and reapplication of brake force when the system detects wheelslide) was activated almost continuously during the approach. This is consistent with a coefficient of friction severely degraded by light rain on leaf-mulch contamination of the rail head.

115 Earlier reports of minor buffer stop collisions, causing no injury or damage to the trains (and therefore strictly not reportable) and of overshot platforms, had tended to be attributed to mishandling of the brake on new and unfamiliar units. Leaf mulch coated tyres of disc braked wheelsets has been a familiar phenomenon since the widespread introduction of this equipment. Some trains did not actuate track circuits (TCs) on lines in wooded areas in late autumn and various methods were used to improve the situation, including the adoption by Regional Railways on certain lines, of hybrid (Class 156/158) DMU with conventional clasp brakes 'scrubbing' the tyres at one end and disc brakes at the other.

116 HMRI undertook an investigation of the Slough accident and other apparently related incidents and discussed mitigating measures with BR and Railtrack. BR and Railtrack have taken the issue of low adhesion very seriously and formed a joint 'Low Adhesion Working Group' to co-ordinate and disseminate best practice and advice on preventing risk from low adhesion. It has produced a newsletter called *Gripping stuff* and a new video film about driving during low adhesion conditions, as well as recommending other control measures. The BR Safety Directorate's August 1995 newsletter *Safety focus* also led with a front-page article reminding managers of the steps they should be taking to be prepared for the season when extremely low adhesion is likely.

Derailments

117 There was a total increase of 36 reported derailments (BR/RT +25, LUL +6, Trams +4, Other +1) amounting to one less passenger train derailment and 37 more freight train derailments. See Appendix 3 for details.

118 On *8 September 1994*, on a day on which Railtrack signalmen were on strike and supervisory staff were manning signal-boxes, the 16.38 Victoria to Orpington was terminated at *Bickley* (RTSZ), Kent, because of a late start from Victoria and the loss of the data link between Orpington and Ashford IECC. It was to shunt forward, stop in advance of the crossover some 300 yards beyond the station, out of sight round a left-hand curve, then reverse over this crossover back into the station before returning to Victoria in passenger service. During the time that this movement was being conducted and before the driver had reached the rear cab, the next train, the 17.13 Blackfriars to Sevenoaks, had arrived at Bickley, overrunning the driver

Derailment at Hungerford on 5 September 1994

only operation (DOO) monitors. To ensure that the passengers were safely clear of the doors, this driver had to lean over to the right-hand side of the cab. He then closed the doors and started his train against the starting signal at Danger because he could not see its aspect from where he had stopped. Beyond the station, the Sevenoaks train ran through the trailing crossover which had, by then, been reversed for the shunt move of the previous train. On seeing the previous train ahead of him, the driver of the following one made an emergency brake application and, thinking that the train ahead was approaching his on the wrong line, reversed and derailed his train on the crossover that he had just burst. This derailment was entirely the fault of the driver of the Blackfriars to Sevenoaks train and, having confirmed that culpability by a series of tests, the Inspectorate left corrective action in the hands of the Operator.

119 On *27 June 1994*, the 16.33 London King's Cross to Glasgow Class 1 parcels train was derailed in the sharp curve at *Morpeth* (RTEC), Northumberland. It was calculated that the train was travelling considerably in excess of the permitted maximum speed of 50 mile/h. Much thought has been given to the circumstances of this accident and to means of preventing a similar accident in future. The Inspectorate has remained in discussion with Railtrack regarding the optimum response but at the time of writing, this has not been finalised.

120 A privately owned train carrying stone from Whatley Quarry to Southall became derailed between *Hungerford* and *Kintbury* (RTGW), Berkshire, when an axle broke on *5 September 1994*. The Inspectorate was concerned about this failure for several reasons, not least of which was the relatively new design of the bogie. The broken axle was sent to the Health and Safety Laboratories in Sheffield for testing and these wagons were taken out of traffic. Submissions have subsequently been made to the Inspectorate by BR Engineering Link, the controllers of the wagon fleet, with detailed proposals for returning the axles to service under a strict safety management regime.

121 The 4-wheel car 55782 of Railbus DMU 142 086, built by BREL Derby in 1987, became derailed at *Leeds* (RTNE), West Yorkshire, on *25 March 1995*, while working the 10.49 Leeds to Carlisle service. The cause was a cracked wheel which had moved inboard on its axle.

122 The 04.02 Wembley European Freight Operations Centre to Dollands Moor (for European traffic via Eurotunnel) and Dover Town was stopped out of course at *Pluckley* (RTSZ), Kent, when the driver realised that something was wrong, at 06.00 on *18 August 1994*. Inspecting his train, he discovered that the frame of a privately owned bogie flat wagon had failed and was, at one point, resting on the sleepers. This caused the trailing wheels to be lifted off the rails, and had derailed the wagon. The Derailment

The derailed wagons which had been carrying steel coils at Elsham on 14 March 1995

Investigation Team of British Rail Research investigated the circumstances to find the cause of this derailment.

123 Built in France and introduced into service in 1988, the wagon was equipped with a flexible sliding hood to cover the steel coils normally carried in five cradles fitted to the deck. At the time of the accident, it was carrying three coils which had been loaded in Llanwern for a destination in Germany. In the centre cradle was a coil weighing 23.54 tonnes and the adjacent cradles were each loaded with a coil of between 15 and 16 tonnes. It was immediately apparent that the wagon had failed because the load was incorrectly distributed.

124 Railfreight Distribution has initiated a programme of detailed inspection of all

wagons with similar characteristics to ensure that no more of them have suffered distortion from overstress and that, beneath their canopies, wagons have been properly loaded.

125 Five 100-tonne fuel oil tank wagons of the 04.45 Port Clarence to Bedworth oil train were derailed at *Sandiacre* (RTMZ), west of Nottingham, by a broken rail, on *4 January 1995*. Three of the wagons fell upon their sides and fuel oil contaminated the area. The National Rivers Authority quickly joined police and the Fire Service on site to minimise the spillage. Much disruption was caused by a signal cable being severed in the accident.

126 An illustration of how several relatively minor factors, each of which may be of little consequence on its own, when combined can lead to an accident, was displayed on *14 March*

Table 7   Significant derailments

Year	Total	Passenger trains	Non-passenger trains	Basic causes		
				Staff error	Technical defects	Other causes
1989	92	32	60	28	56	8
1990	102	26	76	43	54	5
1991/92	79	23	56	29	41	9
1992/93	98	30	68	35	58	5
1993/94	87	29	58	33	51	3
Average 1989 to 1993/94	92	28	64	34	52	6
1994/95	107	28	79	39	51	17

1995 at *Elsham* (RTNE), Humberside. The 18.00 Grimsby to Tinsley freight train, carrying mainly steel coils on bogie flat wagons, was approaching this small, closed station just west of Wrawby Junction and Barnetby le Wold. The driver would probably not have considered track defects such as dips and twists, even if he had noticed the three wooden sleepers in a run of concrete ones; nor would he have known that there was a defective damper on the leading bogie of BNX Wagon B949508, otherwise he probably would not have allowed his train speed to exceed the Class 8 limits of 35 mile/h. In the event, B949508 was the first of the eight wagons which derailed, scattering large coils of steel around the neighbourhood, luckily injuring nobody, but becoming an unusual problem for the Breakdown Gang.

Running into obstructions

127 There has been an overall reduction of 48 on last year's figures of trains running into obstructions (445 to 397). Level crossing incidents in this category also fell, from 49 to 33.

Animals

128 There were eleven more cases (89 from 78) of trains running into large animals. Typically, damage to fences or gates left open by thoughtless members of the public enable animals to stray onto the railway where, very often, they are killed or maimed, causing great distress, loss and disruption. In extreme cases, where the largest animals are involved, trains can be derailed.

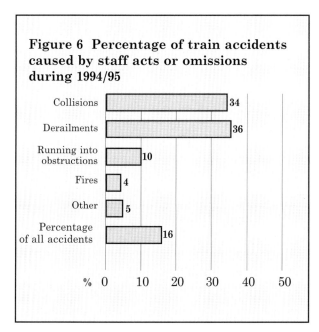

Figure 6 Percentage of train accidents caused by staff acts or omissions during 1994/95

Collisions	34
Derailments	36
Running into obstructions	10
Fires	4
Other	5
Percentage of all accidents	16

% 0   10   20   30   40   50

129 In *September 1994*, a Plymouth to Bristol high-speed train ran into a herd of cows between *Exeter* and *Tiverton* (RTGW), Devon, killing three and injuring several more. Because uninjured cows from the herd were still wandering on the line, recovery operations were protracted. Seven trains were cancelled and six of them were reformed into other services replicating, as far as possible, those stopped by the obstruction. Normal working on both Up and Down lines was restored some seven hours later, after removal of the carcasses. Subsequent investigation revealed that a gate locking mechanism had broken away, allowing it to open freely.

Other obstructions

130 The total number of reports of trains running into 'Other obstructions' decreased by 43 to 275 (see Appendix 3). The worst case was that of the 01.25 Brighton to Three Bridges service on *10 March 1995*. The driver reported that he had struck something in the area of *Maidenbower footpath crossing* (near Balcombe Tunnel Junction - midway between Three Bridges and Balcombe) (RTSZ), West Sussex. The driver of the next Down train confirmed that a motor car was on the railway beside the M23 road bridge and that there were people inside it. The emergency services were called and current was discharged from all lines in the vicinity. The Railtrack South local Field Manager attended and reported that the motor car, containing one live and one dead person, was beside the line. As far as could be determined, it had been involved in an accident on the road above the railway and had landed on the Up Slow line and was then struck by a train.

131 Another road vehicle was struck by a train in quite different circumstances on *10 September 1994*. The 06.37 Southport to Rochdale DMU passenger train (142 004) struck a road vehicle on the running line between *Atherton* and *Walkden* (RTNW), Greater Manchester. It had been burnt out and abandoned. Before striking the wreck, the train had been running at line speed (50 mile/h), but the driver, on seeing the obstruction, made an emergency brake application, reducing the speed of impact to about 30 mile/h. Although the DMU was immobilised, there were fortunately no injuries to passengers or crew. An extensive police investigation has failed to identify the culprit.

132 Commentary on obstructions deliberately placed on the line can be found in Chapter 13.

Chapter 4 LEVEL CROSSINGS

Key facts

- Thirteen members of the public (excluding trespassers and suicides) were killed at level crossings, down one from last year
- Reduction of 9% in train and movement accidents compared with last year
- Three drivers of road vehicles killed by trains running into vehicles
- Accidents at footpath crossings increased by three from seven to ten

General

133 The number of accidents and reported system failures at each type of level crossing during the year commencing 1 April 1994 is given in Table 8. The accidents included are train and movement accidents, as defined in the introduction. Reported system failures are those incidents not giving rise to an accident but which are required to be reported, for example a train running onto a protected level crossing when not authorised to do so, or crossing equipment failing to operate correctly and providing a reduced level of crossing protection.

134 There has been a reduction of 9% (from 66 to 60) in the number of train and movement accidents at level crossings, compared with the previous reporting year, and the total is at its second lowest level for the last 11 years. This continues the downward trend shown by Figure 7 and is lower than the average for the last eight years. The total number of reported

Table 8   Accidents at level crossings

	Total	Protected Manual: MG	MCB	MCB with CCTV	Automatic: AHB	ABCL	AOCR	AOCL	UWC with MWL	Unprotected Manual: UWC	UWC with T	OC	FP
Railtrack:													
Number of crossings													
At 31 Mar 94	8966	281	300	304	459	30	2	166	141	3302	1257	65	2659
At 31 Mar 95	8813	306	277	314	461	27	1	160	114	3209	1209	62	2673
Number of accidents*													
1993/94	61	9	-	-	12	-	-	9	4	12	7	1	7
1994/95	58	8	2	1	4	-	-	7	3	8	14	1	10
Number of system failures†													
1993/94	28	2	6	3	7	-	-	-	8	-	-	-	2
1994/95	54	13	6	4	13	2	-	2	2	-	12	-	-
Other railways:													
Number of accidents*													
1993/94	5	-	-	-	-	-	-	2	-	3	-	-	-
1994/95	2	-	-	-	-	-	-	-	-	-	-	2	-
Number of system failures†													
1993/94	1	-	-	-	-	-	-	-	-	-	-	1	-
1994/95	-	-	-	-	-	-	-	-	-	-	-	-	-

Note: See Appendix 9 for abbreviations used for types of level crossings.

* Train and movement accidents only as defined in Chapter 1.

† Defined as an occasion, not resulting in a train accident, when a train runs onto a protected level crossing when not authorised to do so or when the level crossing equipment fails to operate correctly.

system failures is 54, an increase of 25 from 29 last year. This increase is attributable to better reporting by the railways of wrong side failures (WSF). These were first introduced in 1991 on a voluntary basis and since then the number of level crossing WSF notifications have increased.

135 The figures for the number of crossings shown in Table 8 are provided by Railtrack PLC. The number of crossings on other railways is not shown although reference is made to accidents occurring on these railways and these are shown in the lower part of Table 8. The number of crossings in some categories may appear to vary from those previously recorded. These fluctuations arise as a result of the following factors:

(a) railways closing some private vehicular crossings;

(b) conversion from one type of crossing protection to another;

(c) a reduction in status of some crossings, for example from 'user-worked vehicular crossing' to 'footpath crossing'.

136 The casualties arising from the accidents at level crossings are given in Table 9. These casualty figures include all personal injuries sustained in train accidents and both movement and non-movement accidents, but exclude trespassers and suicides.

Manually-operated gated crossings (MG)

137 Eight train accidents at manually-controlled gated crossings were reported in this year. Five of these involved trains running into gates, either due to driver's error in failing to stop short of the crossing or insecure gates being blown into the paths of trains. One was caused by runaway wagons from a siding.

138 A diesel multiple unit (DMU) struck the mudguard of a cycle and narrowly missed the school child wheeling it at *Blue Gowts Level Crossing* near Spalding, Lincolnshire, on *10 March 1995*. The child was wearing audio headphones at the time of the accident and was seen running away from the crossing after the accident, leaving behind the damaged cycle. It was believed the child might have gained access onto the crossing through the pedestrian gate which was found to be defective. The gate was subsequently repaired.

139 *Motts Lane Level Crossing*, Witham, Suffolk, was the scene of the single movement accident which happened on *4 February 1995* where a pedestrian was fatally injured. A verdict of accidental death was returned. The gates of the vehicular crossing are normally kept closed across the road but with free pedestrian wicket gates on both sides. Telephones are provided for people wishing to use the crossing to summon the crossing keeper who is located at a nearby gated crossing. There has been a proposal to reduce

Figure 7 Level crossing accidents 1984 - 1995

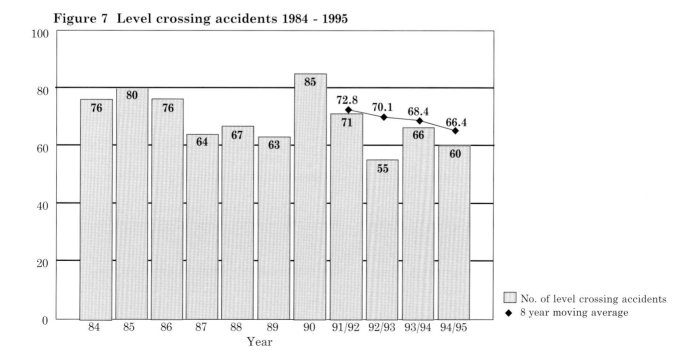

Table 9   Casualties in level crossing accidents - all railways 1994/95

	Protected								Unprotected			
	Manual:			Automatic:					Manual:			
	MG	MCB	MCB with CCTV	AHB	ABCL	AOCR	AOCL	UWC with MWL	UWC	UWC with T	OC	FP
Killed:												
Passengers	-	-	-	-	-	-	-	-	-	-	-	-
Staff	-	-	-	-	-	-	-	-	-	-	-	-
Occupants of road vehicle	-	-	-	1 (2)	-	-	- (1)	1	- (1)	1 (1)	-	-
Pedestrians	1	-	-	- (2)	-	-	1	1 (1)	1	2 (1)	-	4 (5)
Killed total 13 (14)	1	-	-	1 (4)	-	-	1 (1)	2 (1)	1 (1)	3 (2)	-	4 (5)
Injured:												
Passengers	-	-	-	4	-	-	- (2)	-	-	-	-	-
Staff	1 (1)	1	1	2 (1)	-	-	2 (4)	- (1)	1 (6)	7 (2)	- (2)	2 (1)
Occupants of road vehicle	-	-	1	2 (6)	-	-	8 (3)	-	2 (5)	1	-	-
Pedestrians	- (1)	1	3 (5)	- (1)	-	-	-	- (1)	1 (2)	-	-	1 (1)
Injured total 41 (45)	1 (2)	2	5 (5)	8 (8)	-	-	10 (9)	- (2)	4 (13)	8 (2)	- (2)	3 (2)

Figures in brackets refer to last year
Trespassers and suicides are not included in this table

the status of this crossing to a bridle-way and provide MWL as part of a resignalling scheme. Unfortunately, this has not come to fruition otherwise this tragic accident might have been avoided.

140 A crossing keeper suffered broken ribs on *15 March 1995* in a non-movement accident at *High Eggborough Level Crossing*, near Selby, North Yorkshire, when high winds blew the crossing gate against him.

141 Thirteen incidents of system failure were reported. One of these involved a ballast train running onto the crossing when not authorised to do so during a possession of the line by engineering staff. The remaining incidents either involved defective gates, wicket gates, bells, telephones or interlocking mechanisms between the crossing gates and the protecting signals.

Manually-controlled barrier crossings (MCB)

142 There were altogether one train accident, two movement accidents, seven non-movement accidents and ten incidents of system failure reported at manually-controlled barrier crossings, monitored either directly (MCB) or by means of closed-circuit television (CCTV).

143 The single train accident occurred on *3 August 1994* at *Deganwy (MCB) Level Crossing* near Llandudno station, Gwynedd, on the Crewe to Holyhead line when a car illegally parked between the barriers and foul of the line was struck by a DMU. The train driver suffered shock as a result.

144 Of the seven non-movement accidents, one occurred at an MCB and the remainder at CCTV crossings. Five involved falls by cyclists

Accident at Llanboidy Level Crossing on 27 April 1994. The damage caused to a DMU colliding with a JCB
PHOTOGRAPHS COURTESY OF BRITISH TRANSPORT POLICE

and pedestrians, who all suffered injuries, due to defects on the crossing surface. Two pedestrians were injured when hit by a ripped off barrier boom, after the barrier had dropped on top of a lorry due to a momentary loss of power supply.

145 Of the ten incidents of system failure, three involved trains running onto a CCTV crossing when not authorised to do so. Two were due to train driver's error in passing the protecting signal at Danger and one involved the failure of the signalman to lower the barriers before authorising a train to pass a protecting signal at Danger. The remaining seven incidents involved failure of either track circuits, relays, barrier machines, wicket gates or interlocking mechanisms between the barriers and the protecting signals.

Automatic half-barrier crossings (AHB)

146 Four train accidents and thirteen system failures were reported at automatic half-barrier crossings.

147 Last year's report mentioned that a train accident occurred at *Llanboidy Level Crossing*, near Fishguard Harbour, Dyfed, on *27 March 1994*. In fact, the accident happened on *27 April 1994*. A DMU travelling at around 70 mile/h collided with a JCB excavating machine. The JCB was carrying out roadworks, next to the barrier machine, on behalf of Dyfed County Council Highways Department. Four train passengers were injured, one with a broken leg, the train driver suffered shock and the JCB operator was badly bruised. Dyfed County Council was subsequently prosecuted by HMRI, found guilty and was fined £3000 with £2000 costs. The figures in Tables 8 and 9 have been amended to reflect the error.

148 The driver of a road vehicle and the train driver both suffered shock but escaped injury when the road vehicle crashed through the lowered barrier and was struck by a train at *Thorne Moorends Level Crossing* near Goole, Humberside, on *1 August 1994*. A driver was killed when her car collided with a DMU at *Eddington Goods Level Crossing*, near Tutbury, Derbyshire, on *15 November 1994*. It was considered that the low and bright sunshine on the day of the accident was a contributing factor and a verdict of accidental death was reached at the Coroner's inquest.

149 Of the 13 incidents of system failure, nine involved trains running onto crossings when not authorised to do so. One incident occurred as a result of a signal being passed at Danger due to slippery rail conditions and the other eight incidents all occurred when the crossings were under local control. Three were due to train drivers who proceeded over the crossings without receiving an appropriate handsignal from the crossing attendants. Another was caused by a train driver's failure to slow down, despite being cautioned by the signalman and advised that the crossing was under local control, when he observed that the lineside signal on the approach to the crossing was at green. A special instruction has since been issued to set the signals at caution on the approaches to crossings which are under local control to prevent similar incidents.

150 On *18 April 1994*, a relief signalman on his way home observed that the barriers at *Asfordby Level Crossing*, near Frisby, Leicestershire, had failed, and requested permission from the signalman at Frisby signal-box to put the crossing under local control. The signalman at Frisby signal-box agreed but failed to notify him that a train was approaching the crossing and also failed to caution the train driver. As a result a near miss occurred between the train and a road vehicle.

151 On *8 September 1994*, a DMU passed over *Sawley Level Crossing*, near Long Eaton, Derbyshire, with the barriers in the raised position. It was revealed that the crossing had been placed on local control by an S&T fault team but without the authority of the signalman. The failure of the fault team to follow standard procedures prior to carrying out works at an automatic crossing gave rise to the incident.

152 Contamination and low resistance of insulation on relay bases, which control the crossing equipment, gave rise to an incident where a barrier in the process of rising fell on to a road vehicle. Two other incidents which involved the failure of the barriers to lower were reported. These were due to condensation and a worn pin in the barrier mechanism respectively.

153 There were five alleged incidents reported by train drivers concerning the barriers being in the raised position when their trains passed over certain AHB crossings. After extensive testing of the crossing equipment, no defects could be found. This kind of incident reinforces the Inspectorate's belief that it is prudent to install recorders at automatic crossings to detect such intermittent faults. This was also referred to in last year's report.

Automatic barrier crossings locally monitored (ABCL)

154 Two incidents of system failure were reported at locally monitored automatic barrier crossings.

155 One occurred at *Cilyrychen Level Crossing*, near Pantyffynnon, Dyfed, on *26 September 1994*, where a train ran onto the crossing when not authorised to do so. An internal inquiry by the railway, revealed that the incident was attributed to a number of causes. First, the flashing red light which indicates to the train driver that the crossing was not operating correctly was found to be of very low intensity and of severely restricted visibility. Secondly, a group of S&T technicians were carrying out routine testing works at the crossing which prevented its automatic operation on the approach of the train.

156 The second incident happened on *19 July 1994* at *Rawcliffe Level Crossing*, near Goole, Humberside, when an on-track machine went on to the crossing without authority and narrowly missed a bus.

Automatic open crossings remotely monitored (AOCR)

157 No incidents were reported at the only remaining remotely monitored automatic open crossing.

Automatic open crossings locally monitored (AOCL)

158 There were six train accidents, one movement accident and two incidents of system failure reported at automatic open crossings locally monitored.

159 All the train accidents occurred due to failure of drivers of road vehicles to stop at red flashing traffic light signals resulting in collisions with trains. As a result of these accidents, eight occupants of road vehicles and two members of staff suffered injuries.

160 The driver of a road vehicle escaped injury when her car collided with a train at *Botolphs Bridge Road Level Crossing* near Hythe, Kent, on the RH & DR on *4 June 1994*. A similar accident happened on *29 January 1995* at *Dalfaber Level Crossing* near Aviemore, Highland Region, on the Strathspey Railway. The driver allegedly claimed she saw the flashing red road traffic light signals but continued to proceed as the 'barriers had not been lowered'. The lack of understanding of road traffic signs by road vehicle drivers is of concern to the Inspectorate and ways of educating the public to improve their understanding are being considered.

161 A lorry driver escaped injury after striking a train at *Lime Kiln Level Crossing* near Woodbridge, Suffolk, on the East Suffolk line on *21 September 1994*. The lorry driver claimed he was blinded by the low sun. Another accident occurred on *21 December 1994* at *Brampton Level Crossing*, between Halesworth and Brampton Stations, again on the East Suffolk line where the driver of a minibus and six children on board suffered injuries as a result of a collision with a train.

162 While an engineer's on-track machine was traversing *Tongues Level Crossing* within Grangemouth Oil Terminal, Central Region Scotland, on *7 February 1995*, it was struck by a road tanker loaded with diesel fuel. Fortunately, no derailment occurred, but one set of the road traffic light signals was demolished. The driver of the tanker and the two train crew suffered shock as a result. The other accident happened on *7 March 1995* when a car was struck by a freight train at *Holywell Level Crossing* near Newsham; there were no injuries.

163 The single movement accident happened on *15 May 1994* at *South Drive Level Crossing* between Pelaw and Jarrow stations on the Tyne and Wear Metro. An elderly man was struck and fatally injured by a train. A coroner's verdict of accidental death was returned.

164 Of the two incidents of system failure, one was reported by a member of public who saw that the road traffic light signals failed to show when a train passed over the crossing. The other involved a train running onto the crossing when not authorised to do so. Investigations into these two incidents are still in progress.

Crossings equipped with miniature warning lights (UWC and MWL)

165 One train accident, two movement accidents and two system failures were reported at crossings equipped with miniature warning lights.

166 The train accident happened on *21 September 1994* at *Gardners Level Crossing* between Stanford-le-Hope and Pitsea stations, Essex on the LTS line where an EMU collided with a road vehicle. Five out of eight coaches of the train were derailed and the driver of the road vehicle was fatally injured. The cause of the accident was misuse of the crossing by the driver of the road vehicle. A verdict of accidental death was returned.

167 One of the movement accidents occurred on *14 April 1994* at *Whitelaw Level Crossing* between Wester Hailes and Curriehill stations, Lothian, on the Edinburgh to Glasgow via Shotts line. A man, classified as a trespasser by the Procurator Fiscal, at the Fatal Accidents and Sudden Deaths Inquiry, was killed by a DMU.

168 In one of the two incidents of system failure, it was alleged that a train went over a crossing with the MWL at green. No fault could be found with the equipment and the failure was attributed to rust contaminated rails. The remaining incident was due to a defective battery for the telephone provided.

User-worked gated crossings (UWC)

169 Five train accidents were reported. Three of them were collisions between road vehicles and trains, one involved a collision with a bicycle and the other involved a train striking an out of gauge obstruction on the crossing.

170 On *31 May 1994*, a road vehicle was struck by a DMU at *Bilbster Level Crossing* near Wick, Highland Region, Scotland. Fortunately no one was injured. Subsequent investigation revealed that the driver of the road vehicle had been distracted and failed to observe an approaching train and drove into the collision.

171 On *20 June 1994*, another train accident took place at *Marrel Level Crossing*, near Helmsdale, again on the Inverness to Wick line. The driver of a road vehicle sustained injuries after his car stalled on the crossing and was struck by a train. The third accident occurred on *16 December 1994* when a Royal Mail van was struck by a train at *Whitepark Level Crossing* near Stranraer, Dumfries and Galloway, Scotland. The driver of the van sustained injuries and the train driver suffered from shock as a result.

172 Three movement accidents were reported, two of which resulted in deaths and one in major injuries. On *18 May 1994*, a woman was struck and killed by a train at *Ty Gwyn Level Crossing* near Abergele, Clwyd. On the day of the accident, part of the crossing timber deck had been removed for engineering work. The deceased had moved to live in the surrounding area on the day before and was not familiar with the crossing. A verdict of accidental death was returned.

173 A man, classified as a trespasser, was seriously injured after he was struck by a train when he was trespassing on the line near *Cadwell Level Crossing*, near Hitchin, Hertfordshire, on *15 July 1994*. A verdict of suicide was returned for the remaining fatal accident at *Powderham Level Crossing*, near Exeter, Devon on *19 July 1994*.

User-worked crossings with telephones (UWC with T)

174 There were nine train accidents, five movement accidents and twelve incidents of system failure reported at user-worked crossings with telephones. Of the nine train accidents, five were collisions between trains and road vehicles, two involved animals being struck by trains, one involved a train striking an out of gauge obstruction and the remaining accident was a collision with concrete troughing placed by vandals.

175 In all five accidents that involved collisions between trains and road vehicles, drivers of road vehicles failed to use the phones provided at the crossings to request permission to cross. On *10 May 1994*, an elderly man suffered shock after his car was struck by an EMU at *Vale Wood Level Crossing* near Billingshurst, West Sussex. He was subsequently cautioned by the BTP. The driver of a tractor was prosecuted by the BTP and fined £4000 for failing to use the telephones at *Worlingham Level Crossing*, near Beccles, Suffolk. A collision occurred between a train and his empty cattle trailer on *8 July 1994*. Fortunately no one was injured in the accident.

176 A driver was disqualified from driving for 12 months and fined £250 for causing a collision between her car and a train on *21 July 1994* at *Elm Grove Level Crossing* near Hoylake, Merseyside. Another driver was less fortunate and was fatally injured after her car collided with a train on *16 November 1994* at *Carters Level Crossing* near Teesside Airport, County Durham. The drivers of both trains suffered shock as a result. The inquest returned a verdict of death by misadventure. On *3 February 1995*, the driver of a tractor escaped injuries after his tractor was struck a glancing blow by a train at *Easter Dalguise Level Crossing* near Inverness, Highland Region. He was in the process of reversing the tractor clear of the line when the collision took place.

177 A horse was killed at *Underhill Level Crossing*, between Green Road and Millom stations, Cumbria on *18 July 1994*. The owner of the horse, who was leading it over the crossing at the time of the accident, failed to phone for permission to cross. Seven cows were struck and killed on *9 August 1994* at *Sack Lane Level Crossing* near Bognor Regis, West Sussex. The signalman thought the farmer had contacted him from a different crossing to request permission to cross. This accident illustrates that any communication from a crossing to the signalman must be absolutely clear and without ambiguity.

178 Of the five movement accidents, two were related to near misses with children playing on the line. These happened at *Pentre Level Crossing*, near Flint, Clwyd and *Melrose Avenue Level Crossing*, near Hoylake, Merseyside, on *19 April 1994* and *7 July 1994* respectively. The third accident occurred at *Clattercote Level Crossing*, near Banbury, Oxfordshire on *8 September 1994* where a train had a near miss with a tractor and trailer. The cause was an error by the signalman in giving the farmer permission to cross while a train was expected in each direction. The train

drivers involved in the above accidents all suffered shock as a result.

179 On *13 August 1994*, an elderly man, who was walking with his dog over *Burgess Drove Level Crossing* near Waterbeach, Cambridgeshire was struck and killed by a DMU. It was revealed at the Coroner's inquest that the deceased was deaf and the accident happened when he ran after his dog at the crossing. A verdict of accidental death was returned.

180 *Melrose Avenue Level Crossing* (see paragraph 178) was the scene of another movement accident where a child aged seven was struck and fatally injured on *28 October 1994*. The child, with his elder brother, was waiting at the crossing for a train to pass but walked into the path of another train in the opposite direction. The elder brother managed to step back but failed to pull his younger brother clear. A verdict of accidental death was returned. Both the train driver and the guard suffered shock.

181 The 12 system failures all related to defective telephones due to flat batteries or cable faults.

182 There were also numerous incidents where it was recorded that telephones were either misused, damaged or even stolen. Of the 31 incidents recorded, eight were caused by vandalism, and the remainder involved phones being left off the hook by irresponsible users. Some notorious locations were *Carr Lane Level Crossing*, Doncaster, South Yorkshire, *Allsops Main Occupation Crossing*, Loughborough, Leicestershire, *Masserellas Level Crossing*, Doncaster, South Yorkshire, *Kirby Muxloe Level Crossing*, Leicester, Leicestershire and *Mount Sorrel Occupation Crossing*, Leicester, Leicestershire. Such irresponsible actions which could lead to extremely dangerous situations for other crossing users and train passengers are to be deplored.

Open crossings (OC)

183 Three train accidents, with no injuries, were reported at open crossings which involved collisions between trains and road vehicles and were all attributed to drivers of road vehicles failing to give way to trains. These accidents happened at *Glanrafon Level Crossing*, near Aberystwyth, Dyfed, on the Vale of Rheidol Railway, *Greatstone Station*

Level Crossing, near New Romney, Kent on the RH & DR, and *Llanion Level Crossing* near Pembroke, Dyfed on *24 May 1994*, *28 August 1994* and *23 November 1994* respectively.

Footpath crossings (FP)

184 One train accident, nine movement accidents and one non-movement accident were reported.

185 The train accident occurred at *Blounts Wood Level Crossing*, between Rayleigh and Hockley stations, Essex on *7 March 1995*, where a train struck out of gauge timber boards, displaced following engineering works. Fortunately no one was injured.

186 Regrettably, nine people were killed at footpath crossings as a result of separate movement accidents this year. Verdicts of suicide were recorded in five cases, two returned open verdicts, with one accidental and one death by misadventure.

187 Besides one of the suicides mentioned above, two other movement accidents happened at *Glebe Way Level Crossing* near Whitstable, Kent, within a four month period. On *8 September 1994*, a 90-year-old man was struck by a train travelling from Whitstable to Faversham. A verdict of accidental death was recorded. A similar accident at the same crossing occurred on *14 October 1994* when an 87-year-old man was struck and killed by a train. An open verdict was returned. In view of these incidents, Railtrack is carrying out a risk assessment at this crossing and the possibility of closure is being examined.

188 A male pedestrian, aged 72, was struck and killed on *15 January 1995* at *Lankesters Level Crossing* near Stowmarket, Suffolk. The train driver reported that the deceased was standing on the crossing with his back to the train. The last movement accident happened on *14 February 1995* at *Harrisons Level Crossing* near Newcastle where a man was fatally injured. The train driver and the conductor suffered shock as a result. A verdict of misadventure was returned.

189 The single non-movement accident happened on *6 April 1994* at *Fleet Level Crossing* between Sunnymeads and Datchet stations, Berkshire. A pedestrian sustained minor injuries after she slipped and fell on the allegedly slippery crossing surface.

Chapter 5   FIRES

Key facts

- Reduction of 17% in the total number of fires reported
- Reduction of 25% in the number of non-train fires
- Arson or vandalism is still the most common single cause of fires
- The most common, non-malicious causes of fire relate to the traction systems
- Fire risks can be reduced by better maintenance (including rubbish clearance) and good working practices

Summary

190 There has been a sharp reduction in reports of fires for the year 1994/5, compared with the previous year. Non-train fires are down from 118 to 88, with the biggest reduction in the categories 'stations on surface' and 'running tunnels'. Train fires are down from 247 to 217 and this resumes the downward trend that was interrupted last year. While there has been considerable improvement, there is still a high incidence of foreseeable and avoidable fires. Inadequate maintenance (including rubbish clearance) and carelessness are avoidable. While railways are the victims and not the initiators of arson attacks, improved vigilance by staff and timely action by British Transport Police has made a significant contribution to extinguishing fires at an early stage and apprehending the culprits. The many dc traction arc originated fires are worrying. There are examples in several sections of this chapter. Greater management effort is needed to reduce the possibility of traction arcs, by ensuring higher standards of maintenance in dc electrified areas.

Lineside fires

191 There was a spate of lineside fires during some hot dry days of summer 1994 when lineside vegetation or rubbish caught fire. The ignition source was generally unknown, but could have been sparks from brakes or traction current, or discarded cigarettes. The most significant number of other lineside fires was associated with dc traction current arcs.

Table 10   Reported fires other than on trains 1994/95

Type of location	BR/ Railtrack	LUL	Tram systems	Other railways	Total
Lineside, bridges etc	58	4	-	-	62
Stations on surface	11	-	-	-	11
Signal-boxes, sub-stations etc	3	-	-	-	3
Other surface locations and neighbouring property	2	-	-	-	2
Running tunnels	2	3	-	-	5
Underground station platforms	2	-	-	-	2
Underground passages, booking halls including tenants' shops etc	-	-	-	-	-
Escalators, passenger lifts etc	1	1	-	-	2
Underground signal-boxes, sub-stations, switchrooms etc	1	-	-	-	1
Underground station offices, staff rooms, service tunnels etc	-	-	-	-	-
Total	**80**	**8**	**-**	**-**	**88**

Note: Different reporting triggers apply above and below ground ie one hour loss of service above ground, half hour loss of service below ground

192 At *Maghull Crossover* (RTNW), Merseyside on *10 May 1994*, the fire brigade attended a fire, which was a result of a traction current arc. A metallic object or debris had been dragged into the gap between the traction and running rails by a tamping machine returning to Kirkdale siding. The resultant short-circuit burnt out two traction cables and traction supply switch boxes, buckled and moved the traction rail through a 5 cm misalignment, burnt a 5 cm gap in the stock rail and burnt out S&T equipment. Repairs took two days.

193 At *Peckham Rye* (RTSZ) on *21 March 1995*, serious arcing occurred between the conductor rail and running rail. Vandals had thrown objects onto the line, which short-circuited the traction current. Severe damage was sustained to the infrastructure, with two sections of running rail melted and the traction rail bent into the air.

Bridge fires

194 There were six fires affecting bridges and viaducts. As in earlier years, not only can the common lineside hazards of rubbish, oil and sparks lead to fires, but so does carelessness or arson. Two fires were of particular note.

195 At *Arnside Viaduct* (RTNW), between Carnforth and Barrow-in-Furness, Cumbria on *5 June 1994*, scaffold boards, being used during repairs under the viaduct, caught light after a hot rivet had been dropped onto the timber. Fortunately, although eight boards were destroyed, the railway structure was not damaged.

196 At *Northfleet* (RTSZ), Kent on *26 February 1995*, arsonists set fire to about a hundred old tyres, which had been stacked under a footpath bridge. This particular site is isolated and has been the subject of vandalism and arson in the past. Railtrack will be more vigilant at such locations.

Fires in stations

197 There were fewer fires in this category for 1994/5 than 1993/4; a reduction from 33 to 13. Arson, carelessness or low maintenance standards were the principal causes. Four of the incidents of note were in Schedule 12 stations (sub-surface), with two of those on the 'Loop Line' and one on the 'Northern Line' within Liverpool.

198 A fire occurred at *Birmingham New Street* (RTWC) on *20 January 1995*. Any fire underground is potentially serious, but New Street also has a shopping complex built over the station. The fire was the result of a stalled diesel locomotive being restarted, immediately underneath a fume extraction vent. Wear within the engine allowed fuel to pass into the exhaust and it 'backfired', sending a sheet of flame upwards, into the vent. Deposits of diesel oil and soot ignited within the ducting. The whole area had to be evacuated while the fire service dealt with the duct fire. This incident emphasises the need to keep exhaust ducts clean.

199 At *Liverpool Central* (Northern Line) (RTNW) on *27 September 1994*, a fire started just inside the tunnel, with smoke drifting into the station. Signalling track circuit equipment and cables were found to have been damaged by arcing between the traction rail and running rail. The cause was thought to be a short-circuit provided by litter, blown into the tunnel from the station. Litter is a known problem on all underground railways and regular clearance, together with any measures to prevent the litter being carried into tunnels, is essential.

200 At *James Street* (Liverpool - Loop Line) (RTNW) on *25 July 1994*, there was a small fire as the result of a life expired insulator 'pot', which supports the conductor rail, exploding. Railtrack have now replaced a considerable number of these 'pots' on the 'Loop Line'.

201 At *James Street* (Liverpool - Loop Line) (RTNW) on *18 August 1994*, a fire started in a 650 V traction cable, as a result of the incorrect storage of materials for use in engineering work. At the time of the incident, the station was closed for two days, due to industrial action. Railtrack has now issued instructions prohibiting such storage without specific authorisation.

202 Two further station fires are noteworthy and occurred in surface stations.

203 It is believed that a fire was started deliberately behind a newspaper kiosk on the station approach at *Lee* (RTSZ), Greater London on *14 September 1994*. The station canopy and fittings were extensively damaged (estimated at £130 000). Two youths were taken into custody in connection with this incident.

204 At *Southport* (RTNW), Merseyside on *8 May 1994*, there was a gas explosion adjacent to a redundant signal-box. This was followed by a fire in a platform canopy. At the time of the explosion, work was in progress, using a bar to break the ground surface. The bar struck a 650 V traction cable and an adjacent $1^1/_4$ in gas pipe. The pipe fractured and escaping gas was lit by sparks. The gas pipe, which ran under the platform canopy, acted as an earth path, leading to the canopy fire. There were, fortunately, no casualties, in spite of the twin hazards of gas and electricity. It re-emphasises the need to take great care, when breaking the ground near railway lines.

Other fires

205 On *22 January 1995*, an arsonist set light to *Selling Signal-box* (RTSZ), Kent. At the time, the box was switched out, with through working between the adjacent boxes on both sides. The resultant damage left the signal-box unusable.

Fires on trains

Key facts

- Reduction of 12% in the number of train fires
- 41% of train fires were the direct result of arson or vandalism

206 There were no major train fires nor casualties from train fires during the reporting year. A common type of fire, specific to diesel trains, originates in the exhaust system. There were 11 fires of this type, of which four were attributed to faulty exhausts. The other seven exhaust fires were significant, in that they had a common cause: the build-up of oil, which ignited as the exhaust system temperature increased. These exhaust oil fires occurred on three Class 56 locomotives and four HST power cars (including an ECS). The practice of leaving diesel engines idling for long periods is believed to be at the root of the problem and had been recognised in earlier years.

Fires on diesel locomotives

207 There were four fires on diesel locomotives hauling passenger trains, including one of the exhaust oil fires to which reference has already been made. There were 20 fires on diesel locomotives hauling freight trains.

Table 11   Number of train fires 1989-1994/95

Year	Passenger train fires	Freight train fires	Total train fires
1989	199	84	283
1990	205	52	257
1991/92	192	33	225
1992/93	178	24	202
1993/94	217	30	247
Five year average	198	45	243
1994/95	169	48	217

Fires on diesel mechanical multiple units

208 There were 31 fires on DMUs, which is the lowest figure in the past five years. This is a reflection of the reduction in the number of older units still in use. It is interesting to note that there were no reported acts of arson on DMUs.

Fires on high-speed trains and diesel electric multiple units

209 There were five fires on HSTs. As already mentioned, three exhaust fires on HSTs were attributable to oil build-up. This compares with four for the previous year. Also, as last year, fires in floor level ventilation grilles on HSTs were blamed on the careless discarding of cigarettes. There were two particular fires of note.

210 A high-speed train was halted at *Didcot Parkway* (GWTOU / RTGW) on *25 April 1994*, when the rear power car was found to be on fire. The fire brigade was called and the line blocked to traffic on the main line, in both directions. Fortunately, all passengers were detrained onto the platform without injury and the fire contained within the power car. Following this fire, it was reported that steps were being taken to redesign engine silencers on HST power cars, to eliminate the potential for oil fires in exhausts.

211 Passengers on a high-speed train had to be evacuated to adjoining coaches, when their coach filled with smoke, while travelling at speed in the *Darlington* area (RTEC) on *8 August 1994*. A cigarette had been dropped in the floor level air conditioning grill, igniting dust etc. The flow of air across the fire helped the combustion and spread the resultant

smoke. The fire extinguished itself once the air-conditioning was turned off.

Fires on electric locomotives

212 There were four fires on electric locomotives hauling passenger trains and one on an engineer's train (battery locomotive, T&W).

213 One incident occurred in the *Channel Tunnel* (ETUK) on *1 January 1995*, when an HGV shuttle train, en route from France to England, developed a fault in the 1500 V cubicle. A power cable came adrift from its crimp, resulting in arcing and a small fire. This was extinguished by the automatic halon system and the incident contained within the high tension cubicle.

Fires on electrical multiple units

214 There were 114 fires on EMUs. These fires generally fall into two broad categories: technical defects, usually involving the traction supply; or vandalism (often arson). When a dc traction supply is short-circuited, either through a technical defect or by vandals placing objects on the line, the resultant current flow may not be sufficient to open the sub-station breakers. The resultant arc produces high temperatures, melting metalwork, igniting any flammable material in the vicinity and producing smoke and toxic fumes. In a tunnel, the potential for injury is considerable and early isolation of the supply essential. Most arson attacks on trains consist of setting light to newspapers under seats or towels in toilet compartments. Fortunately, all such incidents this year have been discovered before a serious fire has developed and in some cases suspects have been apprehended. Two of the more serious fires, one of each type, are described below.

215 A significant fire occurred near *Kensington High Street Station* (LUL District Line) on *5 July 1994*. The seed was sown for the incident about half an hour earlier, near Gloucester Road Station, when a traction motor cover fell from a train and became wedged between the positive rail and running rail. LUL's four rail traction system is designed to handle this kind of fault and a positive earth fault was detected. However, at the time of the incident there was a problem with the control cables, used for remotely controlling sub-stations from the Electrical Control Room. It was not possible to isolate the source of the fault. A second train,

approaching High Street Kensington, struck an arc between the negative shoegear and earth, thus completing a short-circuit of the traction supply. The arc burned with considerable intensity and the quick action of the train operators, both of the affected train and one travelling in the opposite direction, averted injury. Extensive damage to both train and track occurred in the location of the arc. LUL's internal investigation was not able to establish how the cover came to fall from the train or why an arc was struck. More significantly, it did establish that better arc splash barriers were required and maintenance staff were reminded to ensure the integrity of traction related components.

216 On *29 December 1994*, arriving at *Ravensbourne* (RTSZ), Greater London between Sevenoaks and London (Blackfriars), the driver became suspicious of the action of some youths running from the train. He found a fire had been started behind the seat backing onto the cab partition. He managed to extinguish the fire with an on-board extinguisher, but not before there was a small explosion. The vandals had placed a can of lighter fuel with a wick, behind the seat.

Fires on passenger coaches other than multiple units

217 There were 11 fires on passenger coaches, hauled by locomotives. The incidence of these fires has been reducing for the last five years and reflects the increased use of multiple units over locomotive hauled coaches.

Fires on empty coaching stock

218 There were ten fires on empty coaching stock. A particularly noteworthy fire was another dc traction fire, which produced considerable smoke. It emphasises that it is essential for all railway staff to know their responsibilities.

219 As a train, about to enter passenger service, was approaching Platform 15 at *London Victoria* (RTSZ) on *4 October 1994*, a major electrical fault occurred under the train. This resulted in a short-circuit of the traction supply and fire. The train came to rest in the platform with flames and dense smoke coming from its underside. Staff observing the incident arranged for traction current isolation and the call out of the fire brigade. A Railtrack joint inquiry found that the primary cause of the fire was a failure, during maintenance, to secure components of the train-borne

linebreaker correctly. The smoke emitted by the fire, although significant at platform level, was insufficient at first to trigger the sensors that start the station exhaust fans.

Fires on non-passenger vehicles

220 There were 17 fires on non-passenger vehicles. There were three fires worthy of note.

221 Smoke was observed coming from a train of tank wagons containing kerosene, at *Stenson Junction* (RTMZ), Derbyshire on *3 November 1994*. This was caused by brake drag on ten of the wagons. The train was stopped, pending attendance by the wagon maintainer.

222 The timbers on a wagon carrying steel caught fire near *Scunthorpe* (RTNE), Humberside on *20 July 1994*. The driver attempted to extinguish the fire, but had to call for fire brigade assistance. The cause has been attributed to loading excessively hot steel onto the timbers.

223 A fire started within an on track machine at work in *Moncrieffe Tunnel, Perth* (RTSc) Tayside, on *26 February 1995*. All staff were evacuated from the tunnel immediately and the Fire Brigade called. However, six members of a local permanent way squad re-entered the tunnel and were injured by smoke inhalation. They had to be taken to the local hospital and one was detained. This incident highlights the need for adherence to safety procedures in emergency situations and for clearly defined responsibilities and leadership.

Table 12   Number of train fires by type of vehicle 1994/95

Type of vehicle	Passenger train	Freight train	Total
Diesel locomotive	4	20	24
DMU	31	-	31
HST or DEMU	5	-	5
Electric locomotive	4	1	5
EMU	114	-	114
Passenger coaches	11	-	11
Empty coaching stock	-	10	10
Non-passenger vehicles	-	17	17
Total	169	48	217

Table 12A   Number of train fires by type of vehicle 1990 - 1994/95

Type of vehicle	1990	91/92	92/93	93/94	94/95
Diesel locomotive	56	33	25	15	24
DMU	56	56	47	55	31
HST or DEMU	10	12	9	15	5
Electric locomotive	3	1	-	3	5
EMU	99	72	100	124	114
Passenger coaches	25	44	13	15	11
Empty coaching stock	-	-	3	13	10
Non-passenger vehicles	8	7	5	7	17
Total	257	225	202	247	217

Chapter 6 FAILURES

Key facts

- Total failures show an increase of 10 to 1787
- Reduction of six rolling stock failures to 271
- Significant increases in:
  - track buckles from 25 to 46 (a return to around the 10 year average)
  - flooding and landslips from 210 to 283, owing to bad weather
- Signals passed at Danger down from 905 to 830

General

224 Failures in rolling stock have fallen by six in total, a figure which hides an increase of 18 in electric unit failures, mainly power door malfunctions. An increase of 16, to 1516 permanent way and structure failures includes ten more structural failures, 21 more track buckles - at 46, almost double last year's 25, and a one-third increase in flooding and cutting slips etc, up 73 from 210 to 283 (see Appendix 3).

Rolling stock

225 On *13 January 1995*, the driver of the 20.52 *Gillingham to Charing Cross* train, formed of two new Class 465 'Networker' EMU built by ABB, York 1991/94, found that he could obtain traction interlock before the doors had closed. The interlock is designed to prevent the train being moved in service with the doors not properly closed. He immediately reported the matter and the train was taken out of service to its home depot, Slade Green. It was discovered that blocked chemical lavatories, leaking onto electrical control components were causing the failure. A Notice has been issued, warning operators of rolling stock with similar arrangements to beware. Meanwhile the South Eastern Fleet has had urgent remedial modification.

Wrong side signalling failures

226 The classification of wrong side failures (WSF) and the numbers reported by Railtrack, and formerly by BR, in each category are shown in Table 13. The total for 1994/95 of 637 is a notable reduction on the totals for the previous two years. The largest contributions to this reduction were the fall in the numbers of track circuit failures due to various forms of rail contamination, and the fall in number of position light signals failing to display any lights.

227 To appreciate the significance for safety of the number of signalling wrong side failures, it is necessary to bear in mind that the most numerous categories of failure are generally those that entail the least risk of accident. For example, rust or rail surface contamination happens most often on lightly-trafficked lines where trains are too infrequent to keep the rail surfaces clean. On such lines the probability of a collision resulting from the loss of detection of a train is clearly low, as it is unlikely that there would be a second train in a position to make a conflicting movement. Similar considerations apply to track circuit failure due to leaf fall contamination, although to a lesser extent because in some circumstances heavy leaf fall over a short period can cause failures even on quite busy lines.

228 Track circuit failures due to contamination are not always confined to low-risk areas, however. Train wheels may become contaminated so that the train with contaminated wheels may fail to be detected when it runs on to a busier section of line. For example, on *28 October 1994* near *Peterborough, Cambridgeshire*, a train failed to correctly operate 18 track circuits in succession due to leaf contamination on its wheels. It should be noted that this accounts for one incident in Table 13.

229 Overall the number of track circuit failures due to rust or rail surface contamination fell from 107 to 93, and the number due to leaf fall contamination fell from 95 to 79. The improvement is probably due to the continued programme of fitting track circuit actuator interference detectors (TCAID) mentioned in the 1992/93 Annual Report at known problem sites, together with a strategy of vegetation control. It should also be noted that these problems are dependent on weather conditions, and their incidence is thus susceptible to random variations from year to year.

230 The most numerous category in Table 13 is position light signals, which account for almost half of all wrong side failures. These tend to be low-risk failures, as trains approach these signals at low speed, prepared to stop short at a sight of any obstruction on the line ahead.

231 There has been a marked reduction in the incidents of position light signals failing so that no lights are illuminated. This may be the result of a revised maintenance policy or changing lamps before the end of their rated life.

232 There was a reduction from 44 to 25 in the number of occasions when a colour light signal not protected by lamp proving failed with no aspect displayed. Lamp proving is provided on all but a few small areas of older signalling. The reduction of the number of failures in this category is probably a reflection of the progressive modernisation of these areas, the most recent of which was the resignalling of Boat Train Route 1.

233 Although relatively few in number, failures due to design, test, installation or maintenance deficiencies, of which there were nine for track circuits and 26 for other equipment, account for a significant part of the overall risk from wrong side failure. Such failures are not confined to lightly used lines or low speed movements, and there may be no other means of protection or mitigation of the failure. On *8 October 1994* at *Bow Junction* (RTEA), near Stratford, East London an error in wiring alterations prevented a signal from going back to Danger although it should have done so to protect a train ahead of it. At *Ruscombe* (RTGW), Berkshire on *23 August 1994* the detection of a train crossing from main to relief lines was lost because of a wiring error made when track circuit equipment which had been disconnected to allow for a ballast cleaning was reconnected. Such errors are not confined to the more traditional technologies. Incorrect design of the data used to configure a solid state interlocking (SSI) to its geographical location caused a signal at *North Wembley* on *21 September 1994* to clear in spite of an emergency replacement button being used to maintain it at Danger.

234 No wrong side signalling failures were reported from any other railways during this period.

Broken rails

235 London Underground reported a total of 21 broken rails in the 12 month period of which 15 were in plain line and six in switches and crossings (S&C). The total is just half of last year's figure with the biggest reduction occurring in breakages in switches and crossings, from 18 down to six.

236 LUL have put a lot of work into tightening their standards of follow-up to the reports from ultrasonic testing and a greater than usual length of older rails was removed from the track in the years 1993/94. They have also reviewed their reporting procedures to try to ensure that they are applied strictly in accordance with the Reporting Order. There is evidence to suggest that rails have been reported as 'broken' in the past few years which should not have been included. There is now a robust system of monitoring and regular reporting of broken rails and reason for cautious optimism that the improvement can be sustained.

237 Docklands Light Railway reported two defects, both associated with switch and crossing work. Strathclyde PTE reported five, all in plain line, and Tyne and Wear Metro one, also in plain line.

238 Broken rails, as with many other types of railway accidents, are reportable under the Railways (Notice of Accidents) Order 1986, in writing, on the appropriate form by the earliest practicable post. This system has changed little since the promulgation of the Regulation of Railways Act 1871. In 1996 these reports will be made under new requirements, following an update of the Reporting of Injuries, Diseases and Dangerous Occurrences Regulations 1985. Eventually it is proposed that the transfer of information will be effected by modern information technology and the Railway Inspectorate and Railtrack are to run a pilot scheme through the 12 months, April 1995 to March 1996.

239 In recent years, broken rail reports have been accepted from British Rail in printed form, as called for, from a computer database and this system has worked satisfactorily. The year under review has seen the setting up of Railtrack with a central Headquarters and ten zones (since reorganised to eight zones), and the British Rail Infrastructure Units, who initially undertook both relaying and maintenance were recently reorganised as Renewal or Maintenance Companies.

Table 13   Wrong side failures of signalling equipment

	1994/95	1993/94	1992/93
Cause of track circuit (TC) failures:			
(a) rust or rail surface contamination	93	107	173
(b) leaf fall contamination	79	95	92
(c) bonding deficiencies or insulation failures	13	11	15
(d) relay defects	5	2	3
(e) cable faults	1	3	2
(f) design, test, installation or maintenance deficiencies	9	18	-
Total TC failures	**200**	**236**	**285**
Other equipment design, installation, maintenance or testing failures	**26**	**21**	**45***
Position light signal failures:			
(a) no lights and not light proved	300	326	310
(b) all three lamps lit at once	1	3	1
(c) signals knocked over	9	11	13
Total position light signal failures	**310**	**340**	**324**
Colour light signals - no aspect ·displayed and unprotected	**25**	**44**	**34**
Automatic level crossing emergency telephone failure	**76**	**88**	**77**
Total all wrong side failures	**637**	**729**	**765**

* Includes one on LUL, one on T&W and one on Metrolink

240 Many changes of personnel with different reporting lines and varying local practices have led to administrative difficulties in producing an annual report of broken rails which can be regarded as absolutely and wholly accurate. There is good reason to believe that the rails in the track have been properly dealt with according to the standards of the Industry, but reporting may be found to be wanting and the final BR/Railtrack published figure of 656 might need to be revised upwards but not, it is hoped, by a significant amount.

241 Accepting that the figures as published are substantially correct, it will be seen that the pattern of recent previous years is little changed. As last year the largest number of BR/Railtrack failures occurred at thermit welded joints (151), the second largest through transverse breaks away from the rail end (149), and the third largest number occurred at rail ends and emanated from bolt holes (102).

242 Breaks at switches and crossings and adjustment switches were down in total to 71 from the high figure of 99 reported in 1993/94.

The busy London commuter lines suffer the majority of failures in S&C.

243 Rail breaks per million train miles showed a reduction to 2.26; the rate of failure of welds was unchanged from the previous year at 12.9 per thousand miles of CWR track, and the rate of S&C failures was reduced from 5 per thousand in 1993/94, to 3.8 per thousand units in track in 1994/95.

244 Two derailments were attributed to broken rails. In December an empty tram became derailed on its way from the *Manchester Depot* to *Victoria Station* (GMML) in the early morning. The danger of pollution following a derailment on goods lines at *Sandiacre* (RTMZ), west of Nottingham, of a diesel tanker on *4 January 1995* led to the involvement of the National Rivers Authority. Neither accident led to personal injury.

245 HMRI intends that the management and reporting of broken rails should be subject to a closer overview by the Inspectorate and this will be initiated in the course of 1995, continuing into 1996.

Track buckles

246 Forty-six track buckles were reported by Railtrack in the summer of 1994. This is an increase of 21 over the previous year. The average number of buckles per year over the past five years is 40; over the last ten years it is 42.

247 Twenty-six buckles occurred in jointed track and 20 in continuous welded rail (CWR) and this pattern of (more or less) half and half has been fairly consistent since the mid-1980s.

248 In 1994 there had been one buckle in jointed track in a platform line at Euston Station on the last day of April, and the second buckle did not occur until 25 May. Then, on 13 June there were eight buckles in the one day with rail temperatures recorded at 40° Celsius in Scotland and Northern England. By the end of June there had been a further ten buckles.

249 Early July saw buckling mostly in Southern and Western England with five occurring on 11 July and eight occurring on

Table 14   Summary of broken rails showing type of break

Type of break	British Rail/ Railtrack		LUL & Docklands		Others		All railways	
1 Breaks in plain line								
At rail ends:								
(a) star cracks at bolt holes	102	(140)	4	(4)	1	(-)	107	(144)
(b) other within 600 mm of C/L	86	(71)	2	(3)	-	(-)	88	(74)
At welded joints:								
(a) flash-butt	17	(10)	-	(2)	-	(-)	17	(12)
(b) thermit	151	(154)	-	(1)	2	(-)	153	(155)
(c) other	-	(3)	-	(2)	-	(-)	-	(5)
Away from rail ends and welds:								
(a) transverse (through any part of rail)	149	(142)	4	(8)	4	(2)	157	(152)
(b) surface defects	16	(20)	3	(2)	-	(-)	19	(22)
(c) other	64	(66)	2	(2)	-	(-)	66	(68)
Plain line total	585	(606)	15	(24)	7	(2)	607	(632)
2 Breaks in switches and crossings	63	(81)	8	(18)	-	(-)	71	(99)
3 Breaks in adjustment switches	8	(12)	-	(-)	-	(-)	8	(12)
Total broken rails	656	(699)	23	(42)	7	(2)	686	(743)

(Figures for 1992/93 are shown in brackets)

12 July. Rail temperatures as high as 44º Celsius were recorded in several locations. By the end of July the number for the year had reached 44, and two buckles on the first day of August completed the total.

250 In 15 cases of the 20 buckles in CWR, the cause was attributed to incorrect stress and in 11 cases of the 20, the buckle was associated with, or in the vicinity of, S&C work.

251 In six cases of the 26 buckles in jointed track there were shortages of ballast, and three buckles occurred where the sleepers had been recently disturbed. The largest single cause of buckling in jointed track was attributed to tight joints, often with an absence of rail anchors.

Damage to bridges by vessels and road vehicles

252 A database of bridge strike incidents created in 1990 by the Department of Transport to advise the Roads Minister is now managed directly by Railtrack and contains over 3300 lines of entry over a period of five years, each representing a single incident. The improved management and reporting is

Table 14A Summary of track buckles British Rail/Railtrack 1992 - 94

Month	Total			CWR			Jointed		
	1992	1993	1994	1992	1993	1994	1992	1993	1994
March	-	2	-	-	2	-	-	-	-
April	-	3	1	-	1	-	-	2	1
May	21	2	1	8	2	-	13	-	1
June	8	14	18	7	7	8	1	7	10
July	2	3	24	1	-	11	1	3	13
August	1	1	2	1	-	1	-	1	1
September	1	-	-	-	-	-	1	-	-
Total	33	25	46	17	12	20	16	13	26

reflected in the statistics set out in Table 15 which show a large increase in the total number of incidents involving low rail bridges. While the number of serious incidents remains in single figures and there is a reduction from 61 to 55 for those incidents classified as potentially serious, the total reported frequency of high vehicles or their loads striking bridges must be viewed with concern. The figures for incidents involving overbridges records a significant reduction in serious events where debris, resulting from a

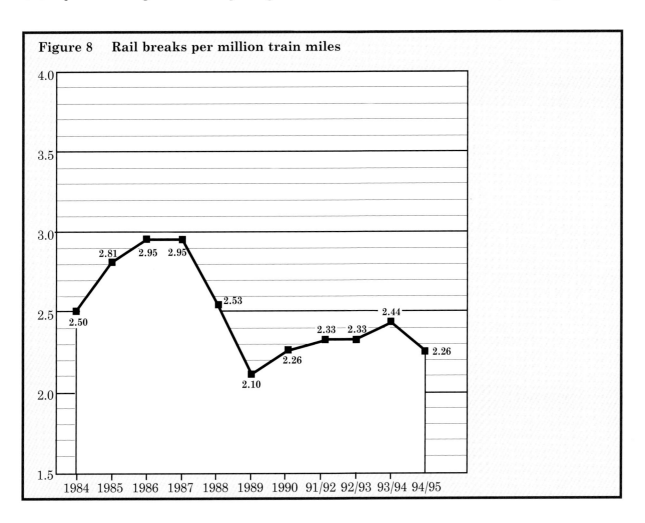

Figure 8   Rail breaks per million train miles

(Line graph showing rail breaks per million train miles from 1984 to 94/95. Values: 1984: 2.50; 1985: 2.81; 1986: 2.95; 1987: 2.95; 1988: 2.53; 1989: 2.10; 1990: 2.26; 91/92: 2.33; 92/93: 2.33; 93/94: 2.44; 94/95: 2.26. Y-axis ranges from 1.5 to 4.0.)

Table 15 Damage to bridges by vessels and road vehicles (British Railways/Railtrack)

	Bridges under railway					Bridges over railway				
	1990	*1991/92	1992/93	1993/94	1994/95	1990	*1991/92	1992/93	1993/94	1994/95
Not serious	790	649	647	750	1039	†125	109	53	50	54
Potentially serious	78	50	58	61	55		25	15	17	18
Serious	11	7	16	5	6	4	4	12	16	9

* Fifteen months
† The breakdown of figures for 1990 is not available

collision with the bridge parapet or wall, has fallen onto the track below. The remaining figures are similar to those recorded for the previous two years.

253 A collision involving a double-decker bus and a low bridge over *West Street* (RTSc), Glasgow on the evening of *18 September 1994*, regrettably resulted in five bus passenger fatalities. In a similar incident, on *29 December*, at *Portland Road, Norwood* (RTSZ), South London, three passengers were injured when a bus was in collision with a bridge.

254 Other railways have suffered too. HM Railway Inspectorate has had reports of six cases of bridge-bashing from London Underground and one from Tyne and Wear Metro during the year. On *6 April 1994*, a bridge over the Bridgnorth to Highley road was struck, north of *Hampton Loade*, Shropshire on the Severn Valley Railway, displacing by about 450 mm the main girders carrying the track, with other damage to wing walls and parapets; train operation over the bridge had to be suspended for two days.

255 The Inspectorate has been pleased to learn of a good response in sales of the *Truckers' atlas of Great Britain* published in 1993 by the Automobile Association and mentioned in last year's report. The atlas clearly identifies the location of most low bridges on major roads to aid route planning.

256 It is a cause for concern that changes in the Vehicle (Construction and Use) Regulations 1986 which have been referred to in the last two Annual Reports have still not been implemented. The intention is that vehicles over 3 m high would be required to have their height displayed in the cab, and that special precautions would be required for vehicles of variable height. This is a DoT responsibility which HSE is actively pursuing with them.

Overhead line equipment

257 At 10.00 on *6 March 1995*, all the circuit-breakers operated for all lines between *Chelford and Cheadle Hulme to Didsbury*, Greater Manchester. They reset, with the exception of a section at *Handforth* (RTNW), between Wilmslow and Cheadle Hulme. Investigation showed that the OLE was down and that a tree branch was resting in one of the structures. One train was stranded and because of the damage to the OLE, both Up and Down lines had to be blocked, with diversions via the Styal line. It took two and a half hours to effect repairs and remove the branch. Gales were blowing at the time.

258 It is still of concern that the OLE has attractions to the perpetrators of vandalism. The following examples have been reported.

259 In *August 1994*, the driver of a Tyne and Wear Metro train reported that the overhead line was completely down at *North Shields*. The service was suspended and a replacement bus service was instituted while repairs were made. The total delay to trains was approximately seven hours. Examination of the damage attributed it to vandalism.

260 In *November 1994*, a train running in the *Winson Green* (RTWC) area of Birmingham brought down the overhead wires. Damage was considerable, including a damaged cantilever at one structure, a broken arm at another, numerous droppers hanging off, catenary strands missing and twists in the contact wires. The unit's pantograph became dislodged and it lost its carbon. It was initially thought that a pigeon had become stuck in the pantograph, but examination by engineers established that an object had been thrown from a road over bridge and wrapped itself round the pantograph, damaging the OLE. Repairs took over 12 hours. A similar incident happened at *Bradwell* (RTMZ), near

Wolverton, Buckinghamshire in *August 1994*, causing approximately one mile of damage and taking over 24 hours to repair.

261 Apart from the above instances where vandalism caused damage to trains and brought down the OLE, minor defects to trains can have the same effect.

262 Retaining bolts for the roof vents on the buffet car of a Manchester to Euston express came adrift, allowing the wind or slip-stream to blow the vents out of position. This was not of itself a serious fault, but coincidentally, a strut insulator on a structure at *Goostrey* (RTNW), near Holmes Chapel, Cheshire, on *22 October 1994* failed and allowed the overhead line to sag and come into contact with the projecting vents, causing damage to the conductor. The defective vents were not spotted until the train's return journey, when it was stopped at Watford because they were seen to be almost contacting the OLE. There were signs that the vents had been struck, and the chain of events earlier in the day then became clear.

Structural failures

263 Considering the number of structures which are present on the railway system, the number of failures reported is very small. Nevertheless, many of them could have had serious consequences had a train been present or approaching at the crucial time when a line became damaged or obstructed. This was brought home most forcibly on *31 January 1995* near *Ais Gill* (RTNE), some six miles south of Kirkby Stephen Station in Cumbria, when flooding in one location and a land-slip in another set the scene for the accident.

264 The collapse of the tunnel under construction for the Heathrow Express link on *21 October 1994*, which caused the collapse of a building in the central area of *Heathrow Airport*, Middlesex, also impacted on the Piccadilly Line of LUL. The new tunnels pass some 50 m below the Hatton Cross to Heathrow Terminals loop. After the collapse, the services were suspended to allow an inspection to take place to see if there had been any damage. A fuller description of the collapse is given in Chapter 1, paragraphs 64 to 68.

265 Other instances of the railway suffering from the actions of others include dislodging of the parapets of road over rail bridges in

road accidents (five), scaffold clips and a steel reinforcing rod falling through glazed roofs from adjacent construction work and contractors placing a heavy crane and its outriggers on an overbridge to do a heavy lift instead of using a rail-mounted crane as had been arranged. All involved some disruption to services while inspections were made or remedial work was carried out.

Signals passed at Danger (SPAD)

266 The arrangement whereby Railtrack/BRB voluntarily make returns of signals passed at Danger to HMRI continues in operation. Fortunately, the vast majority involve stopping within the signal overlap and no more serious consequences.

267 Only eight of the 830 SPADs notified resulted in reportable train accidents, but two of them were serious and involved casualties among passengers and staff - at Cowden (RTSZ), Kent and Wanstead Park (RTEA), Greater London which are described in Chapter 3.

268 Both of these collisions could have been prevented by ATP. HSE is involved in discussions with the industry on the implementation of better systems of train control.

Signals passed at Danger reduction and mitigation (SPADRAM)

269 In the light of the unfavourable conclusions of the cost benefit assessment of ATP, Railtrack and BR undertook a joint study of alternative measures for reducing the risks of SPAD. As a result of that study, the following strategy was developed:

(a) in the short-term, the BR-ATP pilot schemes on the Great Western and Chiltern lines will be brought into full service operation;

(b) in the short- to medium-term, trials will be made of a driver reminder appliance to deal with the problem of starting against red signals, and an enhancement to the existing AWS system to apply the brakes automatically if a train passes a red signal or if a train approaches a red signal at excessive speed;

(c) in the longer term a system of transmission based cab signalling, which will dispense with lineside signals and

which will include automatic train
protection as an integral part of the
system, is to be developed as the
preferred solution for resignalling the
West Coast Main Line and then for
resignalling of other major routes.

270 In addition, measures to improve train
braking performance will be developed and
current initiatives on driver selection, training,
and supervision will be continued. HMRI will
closely monitor the development and
implementation of this strategy, which is
inevitably subject to significant uncertainties
in a number of areas.

Chapter 7 CHANNEL TUNNEL

Key facts

■ Considerable Inspectorate resource involved in Channel Tunnel
■ Safety Case for the tunnel accepted in May 1994
■ Formal opening by Her Majesty the Queen on 6 May 1994

271 The year saw the intensive commissioning and testing of the trains and fixed equipment of the tunnel followed by the progressive introduction of the commercial services. One of the Deputy Chief Inspecting Officers continued as a member of the Intergovernmental Safety Authority with an Assistant Chief Inspecting Officer as his deputy on the Authority.

272 The commissioning and testing was both complex and resource intensive. To be able to satisfy itself that the different types of trains and the required fixed equipment of the tunnel necessary for the safe operation of each type of train was complete and working correctly, the Safety Authority needed to examine the proposed methods of commissioning and testing and then observe those parts of the work identified as the most appropriate.

273 The Inspectorate made available to the Safety Authority a panel of appropriately qualified and experienced inspectors, who could be called on as and when necessary, to observe and report on the work. Similarly, experienced people from other organisations such as the Kent Fire Services were also available to the Safety Authority. The activities of the Inspectorate's observers were organised by an inspector located on the Cheriton terminal site and working alongside the co-ordinator appointed by the Safety Authority.

274 These arrangements provided the assistance the Safety Authority needed, but also met the Inspectorate's own needs in respect of approval under national legislation. In turn the Inspectorate benefited from the information available from the other observers. The necessary national approvals were given in conjunction with the recommendations by the Safety Authority.

275 Commercial services were preceded by a period of trial running for each service. This trial running enabled the national railways and Eurotunnel to demonstrate their readiness in all aspects of the service operation to commence commercial operation.

276 At the request of the Safety Authority, Eurotunnel prepared a Safety Case. The request for the Safety Case and much of its preparation pre-dates the introduction of the Railways (Safety Case) Regulations 1994, and as a result the Eurotunnel submission differed in some aspects from the recommended form under the Safety Case Regulations. As with the approval of the works, members of the Inspectorate were able to assist the Safety Authority in their assessment of the Safety Case as part of their own acceptance procedures. It was considered that the contents of the Eurotunnel Safety Case, while in a different format, adequately met the requirements of the Safety Case Regulations, and the Inspectorate formally accepted the Safety Case on behalf of HSE in May 1994.

277 In addition to the work undertaken by the Inspectorate in approval of the works and acceptance of the Safety Case, the Inspectorate have continued as the enforcing authority of the HSW Act for the UK part of the Channel Tunnel. Care was taken to ensure that the two roles of the Inspectorate were clearly defined and kept separate. In particular, those responsible for the enforcement were able to take a detached overview of the safety of the commissioning and testing in which other members of the Inspectorate were intensively involved.

278 The formal opening of the tunnel took place on 6 May when Her Majesty the Queen, having opened the new International Station at London, Waterloo, boarded a 'Eurostar' train to travel to Folkestone and through the tunnel to the Calais Eurotunnel terminal. The Queen's train arrived at the Calais terminal simultaneously with the train conveying the French President. Following the opening ceremonies in Calais, Her Majesty with the French President travelled through the tunnel to the Folkestone terminal on-board a tourist shuttle.

279 Approval for the national railways freight trains and for the Eurotunnel HGV shuttle trains was given in May 1994. Approval for the introduction of the 'Eurostar' passenger train services was given in August. Approval to the first of the Eurotunnel tourist shuttle services was given in December.

280 Throughout the year the work on the Channel Tunnel has made extensive demands on the resources of the Inspectorate. By utilising the wide-ranging professional expertise of its inspectors from HQ and the field, the Inspectorate was able to respond to them in an effective and timely way.

Chapter 8 LONDON UNDERGROUND LIMITED

Key facts

- Thirty six people killed on LUL, an increase of one on the previous year
- Five passengers killed, the same as 1993/94
- First staff fatalities since 1991/92
- Continued research into platform hazards highlighted a number of measures for further development:
    - closed-circuit television
    - passenger alarms to automatically stop a train departing
    - barriers between carriages to prevent people falling between them
    - emergency train stop devices

Safety management

281 LUL have developed a Corporate Safety and Loss Control Action Plan containing a number of key objectives. Matters of particular interest to HM Railway Inspectorate include the preparation by LUL of their Safety Case, discussions having taken place with the Inspectorate during its development. The aim is to achieve timely submission to, and acceptance from, HSE prior to 28 February 1996.

282 Also of interest are LUL's programme to ensure the requirements of new legislation are met, including the Railways (Safety Critical Work) Regulations 1994, and the aim to reduce lost time injuries to employees - still accounting for almost one third of reported incidents. In addition, LUL is updating and extending its corporate risk assessment to better enable them to target the expenditure of funds. The Inspectorate remains committed in seeking to ensure, for its part, that levels of safety are at least maintained, or improved where it is 'reasonable and practicable' to do so. To this end it is noted, as last year, that engineers may increasingly need to exercise their competence in ensuring the safety of the system and people, should the condition of LUL assets deteriorate.

Revision of Rule Book

283 The delay in implementing the revised rules, or 'procedures', that was reported in last year's report, has continued. An education and communication process was introduced to ensure the revisions could be properly briefed to users and their implementation was rescheduled for 30 April 1995.

Platform hazards

284 A particular area where the Inspectorate and LUL believe improvements in safety can be made concerns the safety of people at stations while boarding and alighting from trains. The outcome of a jointly sponsored risk assessment, conducted by an external consultant towards the end of 1994 and endorsed both by LUL and the Inspectorate, showed that four measures (out of twelve that were studied) are worthy of further development. These are:

(a) closed-circuit television (CCTV) in train cabs to provide drivers with a view of the platform as they enter and leave a station, as well as during the period they are stopped;

(b) existing passenger alarms inside trains to have the facility to automatically keep a train at a platform, or stop it while departing;

(c) barriers between carriages to prevent people falling between them, or a 'sensing' device to detect and immobilise a train should such an incident occur;

(d) emergency train stop devices, operable by platform staff.

285 The Inspectorate is considering what further studies could take place to support the findings of the report and other possible initiatives. Meanwhile, the development by LUL of the measures outlined will be closely monitored.

Accident record

Train accidents

286 LUL has reduced its train accidents to 26 compared with 27 last year. There were three collisions and one derailment of a passenger train, from which no injuries resulted. Twelve incidents were reported of trains running into obstructions. Three incidents of fire or smoke involving rolling stock were reported. Seven involved empty trains that were not in passenger service.

Movement accidents

287 After two years free of employee movement fatalities on LUL, a male track worker was struck and killed by a passenger train at *West Hampstead,* on the Metropolitan Line, on *23 June 1994.* He was one of a gang, the rest of whom had otherwise moved clear following an audible warning sounded as part of the system of work. A verdict of accidental death was recorded by HM Coroner.

288 Thirty-three passengers or members of the public were killed, compared with 35 in the previous year. See Table 16, which includes one non-movement fatality.

289 A 73-year-old man was killed at *Ealing Common*, on the District Line, on *7 September 1994*. He inserted his walking stick between the closing doors of a train and, although there are door-close electrical interlocks fitted to the passenger doors of all LUL trains, their engineering tolerance is such that the door edge rubber strips closed around the walking stick and the 'doors closed' circuit was completed. The train operator, upon receiving a door-closed pilot light and checking that all was apparently in order, started the train. The man who was also carrying a bag of shopping goods, believed to have been on the same arm holding the stick, was unable to let go and was dragged beneath the train. The television monitors have since been upgraded.

290 This accident tragically demonstrates the care that needs to be taken by passengers not to interfere with train doors when they are closing and to ensure that slender parts of belongings, including coats, bags and items such as baby-buggies, do not become trapped in train doors.

291 Late on New Year's Eve, *31 December 1994*, at *Ravenscourt Park* on the District Line,

a man under the influence of alcohol fell onto the track following the departure of the train from which he had alighted. Evidently he lay on the track unnoticed and was struck and killed by the next train entering the platform. The oncoming train driver was unable to see the man in sufficient time to stop his train.

Non-movement accidents

292 A contractor's employee suffered fatal injuries when he fell across live conductor rails at *Theydon Bois* station on the Central Line on *4 July 1994*. He and another person had previously crossed the two tracks to collect some drinking water on what was a warm sunny day. Having returned ahead of his colleague and recrossed the tracks, the victim was in the process of crossing yet again, apparently to assist in carrying the bottled water to their place of work, when he tripped and fell across both conductor rails of the eastbound line. Despite attempts, after the current had been switched off, to resuscitate him, assisted by a waiting passenger at the station, the man succumbed to his injuries. Had the men used the available footbridge situated part-way along the platform this tragic accident would have been avoided. This was the first non-movement fatal accident to a worker since 1991.

Fire and smoke incidents

293 Following the trend in recent years, the number of fire reports has continued to fall. The one exception within the five categories shown in Figure 9 is 'Miscellaneous', where the number has increased from 37 to 40. Although this slight increase is not significant compared with the overall reduction in numbers, the good housekeeping and cleaning regimes need to be maintained so that these figures can be driven down still further. Continued vigilance is also important so that where rubbish can accumulate, including the public areas of stations in the absence (for security reasons) of waste bins, the likelihood of any fire taking hold is minimised.

294 Of the figures shown for 1994/95, only a small number are statutorily reportable, triggered when train services are disrupted for 30 minutes or more underground or for one hour overground. The number of fire reports where no cause was found decreased from 1974 in 1993/94 to 1651.

Table 16   Fatal accidents to passengers on London Underground Limited 1994/95

Type of accident	Total	Inquest verdict:				
		Accident	Misadventure	Open	Suicide	Outstanding
Fall/jump from platform and struck	27	3	1	7	15	1
Struck standing near platform edge	-	-	-	-	-	-
Other movement accidents	1	1	-	-	-	-
Crossing the lines	5	-	-	2	3	-
Non-movement accidents	1	-	-	1	-	-
Total	**34**	**4**	**1**	**10**	**18**	**1**

Table 16A Fatal accidents on London Underground Limited 1990 - 1994/95

Category	1990	1991*	1991/92†	1992/93	1993/94	1994/95	Total
Staff	6	-	2	-	-	2	10
Passengers	7	-	5	2	5	5	24
Trespassers	20	5	23	9	10	11	78
Suicides	13	2	9	18	20	18	80
Total	46	7	39	29	35	36	192

* The figures for 1991 cover the period 1 January 1991 - 31 March 1991
† The figures for 1991/92 have been revised

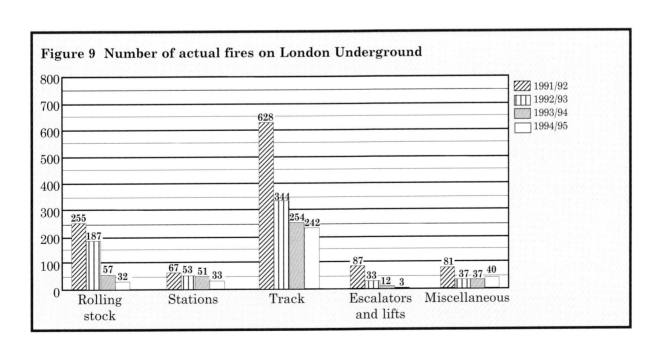

Figure 9 Number of actual fires on London Underground

295 On *5 July 1994*, an earth fault associated with the positive traction current rail at *Gloucester Road* coincided with an earth fault on the negative collector shoe gear of a passenger train approaching *High Street Kensington* station from Earl's Court and an electrical fire resulted. Damage occurred to equipment and cables beneath the front end of the leading vehicle and dense smoke penetrated the driver's cab and passenger area. The traction current was isolated and passengers were detrained through the rear end of the train to walk the short distance to the station. LUL are undertaking some modification work to the underfloor equipment of the Circle Line ('C') stock concerned, but the integrity of the fire-resistant flooring of this refurbished stock was reasonably proven.

Central Line modernisation

296 With the complement of new trains now complete, all Central Line services feature rolling stock whose performance and reliability has begun to exceed that for all other LUL lines. The implementation of automatic train operation (despite this terminology, an operator will always be present at the controls) to enable the maximum number of trains to run safely at optimum speeds, including the provision of ATP, will be phased in from late 1995. Although some associated work on this major project has yet to be completed, progress is being made by LUL on a similar project for the modernisation of the Northern Line. No doubt much will be heard about and reported on this in due course.

Jubilee Line extension

297 Despite the cessation of tunnelling work utilising the New Austrian Tunnelling Method (NATM), following the collapsed excavation at Heathrow on 21 October 1994, other parts of the project have progressed well. The first tunnelling machines were installed in September 1994 and were in place at all major work sites by April 1995, by which time some 40% of tunnelling work had been completed. Structural work on the new Service Control Centre at Neasden was virtually complete by that date, with significant progress also being made to new station structures and alterations to a number of existing stations. As well as ensuring that appropriate safety measures are designed and built into the scheme, which will be necessary to secure HMRI approval on completion, public and staff safety on the existing railway where it is affected by the new works must remain a high priority for LUL to manage and control.

Chapter 9 LIGHT RAPID TRANSIT

Key facts

■ Beckton extension of Docklands Light Railway was opened
■ South Yorkshire Supertram became operational
■ Fifty-one tram accidents reported compared with 44 last year
■ Twenty-nine accidents involving trams running into road vehicles

General

298 At the end of last year HMRI was able to announce two significant steps in the resurgence of light rapid transit systems in this country: the opening of the Beckton extension of the Docklands Light Railway (DLR) bringing the first application of moving block or transmission-based signalling; and the opening of the first phase of the South Yorkshire Supertram System in Sheffield. The Alcatel signalling system has gradually been introduced onto the rest of the DLR so that the whole of the railway now operates on the new signalling.

299 In Sheffield the opening of the spur into Herdings Park just fell into the next reporting year which now leaves only Phase 8 out to Hillsborough and Malin Bridge still to be completed. On 23 May 1994, HRH the Princess Royal formally opened the South Yorkshire Supertram. At that time only Phase 1 was open to traffic and so she had to transfer to other means for the short journey from Park Square

to the Cutler's Hall. However, since then the other phases have progressively been opened so that the system now runs through the city centre. When the environmental works have been completed by the city authorities, Supertram will well demonstrate what can be done to fit a modern tramway system into the urban environment.

300 On a very much reduced scale lies the Wirral Tramway, also known as the Birkenhead Tramway. This short tramway at present runs from the Woodside Terminal as far as the Pacific Road tramshed, a distance of just over 300 m, but plans exist to extend it for a further 400 m. The track uses traditional tramway construction and vintage type traction poles, made from modern materials, support a simple trolley wire overhead current collection system. Two cars, replicas of a 1920s design and built in Hong Kong, form the passenger-carrying fleet. Considerable modification of these vehicles was required before they were acceptable even for the low-speed, limited movement of this tourist

The trams for the South Yorkshire system, which was completed in 1995, were inspected while on trial on the Rheinbahn Tramway, Germany

attraction. This is perhaps a lesson to others who might be tempted to build or import replica trams which do not meet current standards for safe operation. Restorations of genuine historic trams fall into another category. They may be allowed to operate under strictly controlled conditions but, like their replica counterparts, will not be permitted to form part of a modern, urban transport system.

301 The latter remarks do not strictly apply to the operations in Blackpool where many old, but, for these purposes, not historic cars will continue to run. However, encouraged by the Inspectorate, the Blackpool system is beginning to tackle some of the aspects of the system, such as the overhead traction current supply, where the standard of integrity of the system is below that expected today.

302 The Inspectorate is taking a full part by providing advice to those who are actively engaged in extending their systems, such as DLR's extension to Lewisham, and Manchester Metrolink both to Eccles and to the Airport, or who are building or hoping to begin building systems in Birmingham, Leeds, Croydon, Nottingham and South Hampshire. Agreement was reached with the Department of Transport, Energy and Communications in Dublin for the Inspectorate to provide them with technical advice on the proposed Dublin LRT system.

303 The well-publicised remedial works in Mosley Street, Manchester and a number of road traffic accidents in Sheffield, in which the road vehicle has skidded but which did not involve a tramcar, has caused the Inspectorate to look more closely into the problems of the carriageway surface immediately adjacent to tram tracks. The law requires the rails to be level with the surface of the road. This was achievable with the traditional form of construction where the road surface was laid after the track had been laid. Less attention was paid then to the problems of stray currents leaking to earth and also the disruption of other road traffic during repairs to tram tracks was marginally more acceptable. The modern tram rail is laid in a concrete trough and surrounded by some form of polymer. The finished concrete road surface in which the trough is constructed may not be laid sufficiently accurately to follow the exact 'top' required of the rails, particularly on vertical curves. The level of the final pour of the polymer may also not coincide with either the crown of the rail or the surrounding concrete. All of this adds up to a very 'stepped' cross-sectional profile with a skid resistance which varies widely across it. The Inspectorate has commissioned a research contract with the aim of establishing what can reasonably be achieved in cross-sectional skid resistance and relative levels of rail and road surface with a view to being able to give advice on future forms of construction and any remedial work which might be deemed necessary.

Accidents

304 Of the 51 reportable tramway accidents which have involved tramcars, 14 occurred in Blackpool, 27 on Metrolink and ten in Sheffield. There was one other accident in *Blackpool* on *26 February 1995* when an elderly pedestrian stepped out from a newly constructed shelter into the path of an oncoming tram and was killed. The 'bus-stop' pattern shelter had an opaque, not a glass, wall facing the tram, thus concealing from the tram-driver anyone in the shelter. The operator has been asked to consider whether this type of shelter is appropriate to the tramway.

305 It is quite clear from the accidents on Metrolink that there are identifiable black spots where trams and road vehicles run into each other. The junction of Balloon Street and Corporation Street had nine such accidents. Along Mosley Street, including St Peter's Square, a further seven accidents occurred, some of which were on unsignalled junctions. The problems which have arisen on Mosley Street have unfortunately fulfilled the forecast made at the time of the initial approval of the system. These reflect as much as anything the disregard of motorists for road traffic signs and signals, something which no amount of traffic management can completely cure. For example, there is no defence against a car reversing along a bus only lane as occurred in *Mosley Street* on *30 August 1994*.

306 Three out of the ten accidents in Sheffield were minor derailments but a fourth, where the tramway leaves the street for a segregated section at Queens Tower, was a deliberate act of vandalism on *22 March 1995* when a metal bar was wedged in the grooved rail. In contrast to Metrolink, the majority of the other six accidents, which were all low-speed contacts between a tram and a road vehicle, were caused by the tram driver attempting to pass a vehicle parked just foul of the swept path.

307 The majority of the accidents in Blackpool were minor derailments, but there were three collisions, two of which resulted in several minor injuries. On *28 May 1994* a single-deck tram ran into the rear of another single-deck tram which was standing at a stop, unloading passengers. Some 24 people were treated for minor injuries. The driver who failed to stop his tram was found to be responsible and was dismissed. In another incident it was alleged by the driver of a another single-deck tram that a wasp had entered his cab, distracting his attention and was the cause of his car running into the rear of a double-deck tram on *22 August 1994.* Three members of the staff and four passengers suffered minor injuries.

308 Next year will see the completion of the South Yorkshire Supertram System and continuing work on the next systems as well as monitoring the experimental work on the LR55 rail, the TRAM project, the Parry Peoplemover and certain aspects of guided buses.

Chapter 10 MINOR RAILWAYS

Key facts

- There are well in excess of 200 minor railways
- They are quite small: from about 100 yards to 23 miles
- Minor railway trains ran 9 million passenger miles last year

Emergency exercise on the Ffestiniog Railway on 30 October 1994
PHOTOGRAPH COURTESY OF MR STEWART MACFARLANE

General

309 This year has seen the development of a section about minor railways in the new edition of the Inspectorate 'Requirements' (the 'Blue Book') now entitled *Railway safety principles and guidance*. Part 2, Section H covers heritage railways, while details on heritage tramways appear in Section G *Tramways*. The Inspectorate is most grateful for the help of representatives of the Association of Independent Railways (AIR), the Association of Railway Preservation Societies (ARPS) and the National Tramway Museum, who volunteered to be members of the working group drafting the document and offering advice regarding the interests of their members.

310 It was reported last year that AIR and ARPS had combined their strength and expertise under the title Railway Clearing House (RCH) when it was necessary to speak with a united voice in Westminster or Strasbourg or otherwise display their common interests. While it was convenient to adopt such an appropriate railway title, they have subsequently found that the title had not fallen into disuse, and so they have chosen to continue their work under the title Association of Independent Railways and Preservation Societies (AIRPS) from 1996.

311 Several of the most enterprising minor railways conduct emergency exercises to enable their staff to become familiar with some of the difficulties that may have to be faced and to develop a working relationship

with the emergency services. On 30 October 1994, the Ffestiniog Railway mounted such an exercise featuring a motor car that had tried to beat a train across a level crossing near Tan-y-Bwlch, Gwynedd. A two-page account of the action was published in the January 1995 edition of *Railway magazine*. A photograph depicting the scene, taken by Mr Stewart Macfarlane, the FR's operating volunteer co-ordinator who planned the exercise, is reproduced with his permission.

Accidents

312 A fatality occurred in *September 1994* when a man and woman took their dog for a walk along the *West Somerset Railway*. The locomotive crew of the next train saw them and sounded the whistle. The couple stood back on hearing the warning but, as the train passed, their dog leapt onto the line and the woman, in a vain attempt to save it, followed and was struck and killed. Similar examples of trespass are reported by the national railways and once or twice a year they unfortunately lead to deaths.

313 There were two derailments on the Snowdon Mountain Railway (SMR), Gwynedd, during the year. The first, on *26 May 1994*, was at the *Halfway Passing Loop* when one wheelset of diesel locomotive No 12 derailed on unlatched facing points. There was no failure of the rack or pinions and the passengers were in no danger, only suffering the inconvenience of waiting for a relief train. This accident was brought about by a lapse in operating procedures by train crew. This possibility will be eliminated by the installation of semi-automatic operation, as already in service at the Hebron Passing Loop.

314 The second derailment on the SMR occurred at *Hebron Passing Loop* on *23 July 1994*, when unusually hot weather reduced the clearance between the fixed and movable rack sections, preventing the correct movement of the upper set of points and holding the indicator light at Red. It was decided to cross trains by using the loop as a siding and this was done without difficulty. The shunt movement necessitated by this did, however, cause some delay and a decision was made to cool the upper points by pouring water on them from a nearby water course. The next train, which was downhill, was stopped at the points and then closely observed as it moved very slowly over them. As it did so, the leading wheelset of the rear bogie of the coach derailed on a loose rail clip that had jammed

between the movable rack and the stock rail. It is thought that the expansion followed by quick contraction, when cold water was poured onto the assembly, was the reason for displaced rail fastenings. Once again, passengers were inconvenienced but not endangered.

315 One of the most serious incidents during the year involved four members of the catering staff working in a kitchen car who were affected by carbon monoxide inhalation. After medical treatment they recovered. Investigation revealed that no adequate system of inspection or maintenance existed for the six gas-fuelled items of catering equipment. The Railway involved immediately appointed a properly qualified gas engineer to undertake the appropriate inspections and maintenance and reviewed its organisation.

316 Other staff injuries include:

(a) a catering volunteer, who tripped while taking a short cut across a work site and lost the sight of one eye;

(b) a volunteer locomotive cleaner who broke his ankle when he lost his footing helping a colleague investigate a suspicious light and movement during the hours of darkness;

(c) a young man wearing rubber gloves for carriage cleaning, who when asked to help wind a turntable, suffered severe bruising of his hand and lower arm when his gloves caught on the handle and he was forced to the ground;

(d) a driver who was trying to 'notch up' a steam locomotive, the reversing lever of which sprang back, throwing him against the cabside, breaking his arm;

(e) the guard of a loose-coupled goods train who did not brace himself sufficiently when a signal was returned to Danger and suffered a gashed head; and

(f) a shunter who broke his wrist when he fell over while operating hand points.

317 A crane overturned when the rail that it was lifting snagged and the slewing brake slipped. The operator was unable to drop the load in time and the unstabilised crane fell as the load approached 90 degrees from the centre-line of the crane.

318 To reduce the risk to the public from inexperienced and over-enthusiastic drivers, the Inspectorate insists on drivers of passenger trains being at least 21 years old. A certain railway in a remote location, finding that the appropriate staff were unavailable, put a youth of 17 in charge of a passenger train. Incorrectly coupled, the train divided, the automatic brake did not function and the coaches ran backwards into a buffer stop at which point one coach derailed. Fortunately, the speed of impact was quite low, so the passengers suffered no more than bruises and shock.

319 Two level crossing accidents that occurred on minor railways during the year are described in Chapter 4.

320 Derailments caused by vandalism are mentioned in Chapter 13.

Chapter 11 HEALTH AND SAFETY OF WORKERS

Key facts

- Heavy involvement of Inspectorate during signalling staff dispute
- Inspectors started using Safety Cases in inspections and monitoring of safety
- Nine railway staff/contractors killed, an increase of one on the previous year
- Number of staff fatalities on BR/Railtrack fell by one to seven
- Decrease in the number of major and minor injuries
- Three Prohibition and 12 Improvement Notices issued
- Three prosecutions heard involving four defendants; fines imposed totalled £68 000

BR track safety initiative

321 The safety management programme referred to in last year's report reached the implementation stage and the alterations to the Rule Book, which had been discussed in detail by the field Principal Inspectors, became effective on 22 April 1995.

322 Because of the fundamental nature of the changes with alterations to the role of the person in charge of work (PICOW), the introduction of a site warden and the provision of a safe area (Green Zone) in which people who had not been trained in track safety could work, a wide ranging programme of training and briefings was conducted. This was carried out by initially retraining PICOW trainers and then cascading the new rules to all PICOW, including those employed by contractors. Two Inspecting Officers attended PICOW training courses and Inspecting Officers were briefed on the new track safety rules. A new edition of the *Track safety handbook* was published and RIAC completed work on guidance entitled *Railway safety: the prevention of risk to workers on the track*.

323 A design of fencing to mark the danger margin of the Green Zone and two prototype TCODs (track circuit operating devices) to provide protection, were demonstrated to the Inspectorate as a prelude to an application for approval in accordance with section 41 of the Transport and Works Act 1992.

324 A key objective of the new arrangements is to increase the segregation of workers from the hazard of moving trains, and new procedures to facilitate this, while ensuring the necessary level of safety, were introduced. However, they depend upon better planning of work and liaison between maintainers and operators to enable them to be implemented. Early indications are that this new approach has not yet been widely adopted; field inspectors are

monitoring the situation and discussions with BR and Railtrack will continue if the Inspectorate concludes there is room for improvement.

Signalling staff strike

325 A ballot among Rail, Maritime and Transport (RMT) trades union members resulted in a series of one- and two-day strikes between mid-June and the end of September 1994. In the absence of approved schemes of assessment for signalling staff's competence, Railtrack submitted, and the Inspectorate accepted, a list of conditions making up a competence standard for signalling staff. Initially, few trains were operated but as the competence of more managerial staff was assessed, the number of trains was increased.

326 The Inspectorate received representations from both RMT and the Associated Society of Locomotive Engineers and Firemen (ASLEF), about an alleged reduction in safety standards, and meetings were held with Trades Union HQ staff.

327 Allegations were made by RMT members both locally and centrally of individual errors by stand-in signalling staff in dealing with failures of equipment, the taking and giving up of possessions and in setting routes. There were also reports from train drivers, both locally and through their union HQ, of signalling irregularities. The latter are not normally forwarded to the Inspectorate because there is a recognised standard system for providing an explanation to a driver. There was evidence, as presented at the Inquiry into the collision at Newton in 1991, that this system was not operating correctly and the Inspectorate insisted that it be maintained and speeded up.

328 In addition to complaints and reports received locally, Inspecting Officers (IOs)

investigated 118 allegations received centrally from ASLEF and RMT.

329 As well as these investigations, IOs made over 170 visits to signal-boxes on strike days to assess the standard of competence of signalling staff.

330 There were no train accidents caused by stand-in staff, although there were two near-misses. One involved a vehicle being given permission by telephone to use a private level crossing when a train was closely approaching and on another occasion a train was called past a signal at Danger with the route beyond incorrectly set. In some cases allegations made by ASLEF members proved to have involved regular signalmen who were not on strike.

331 In general, the performance was similar to that of regular staff but this was with a considerably reduced train service and for short periods of a day or two only. The Inspectorate objected in one case to staff being rostered for more than twelve hours and to staff being trained by stand-in staff. They reminded Railtrack of the need for the drink and drugs policy to be enforced and for stand-in staff not to work excessive hours by virtue of combining their normal work with their stand-in duties.

The management of safety

332 Reference was made in last year's report to the process of assessing the Railtrack Safety Case and the use of Safety Cases in the monitoring of safety management systems. In the year under report, IOs have assisted with the assessment of the Train Operating and Freight Operating Units' Safety Cases and have begun to use Safety Cases in inspections and monitoring of safety.

Signalling function inspection

333 One example of this work was the inspection of the signalling function, which was conducted in four of the ten Railtrack zones by IOs, assisted by staff from HSE's Accident Prevention Advisory Unit (APAU).

334 The objective was to follow the organisation and responsibilities described in the zone Safety Case for the signalling function, from the Zone Director to the individual signalman and mobile inspector, including their job descriptions and safety responsibility statements. Inspectors would also verify at each stage that the undertakings given in the Safety Case are complied with. At the same time, the way in which the safety management system is maintained was studied, with particular reference to a number of specific subjects. These included the way in which failures and faults are reported and remedied, the safety briefing of signalling staff, the maintenance and issue of documents, such as notices, Rule Books and route setting cards and the way in which occurrence books and other signal-box records are maintained.

335 This type of inspection, which is comparable to a formal or proprietary audit, requires careful planning, a degree of co-ordination in questioning and subjects for discussion, preparation to make appointments to avoid wasted time and action to obtain documents (or to have them readily available) before the actual inspections start. It also takes up considerable resources. In each zone a Principal Inspecting Officer and three IOs were formed into teams of two and allocated some ten working days to the field work, plus the time to write a report and present it to the Zone or Production Director. Because it was the first of its kind, the inspections were staggered so that the experience gained could be passed on and successive improvements made.

336 Because the Safety Case is actually the formalisation of an existing safety regime, as was hoped, no major omissions or errors were found. However, there was evidence of a failure to brief staff, of a failure to involve safety representatives, of slow progress with risk assessment, and of inadequate systems for the repair of faults and failures which did not close the loop from the report of the failure to the report of reinstatement. A number of aspects were found to be well managed including safety auditing. The reports to Zone Directors mentioned both successes and failures, with references to the Safety Case. A summary report will be presented to Railtrack.

Formal HSW Act enforcement action

337 As mentioned in the past, IOs have powers to issue either Improvement or Prohibition Notices (INs or PNs), should persuasion fail or if the danger is very real and not appreciated. The issue of a Notice is always accompanied by the gathering of evidence, in the form of statements, photographs or the opinion of a specialist inspector. In the year being reported on, three Prohibition Notices and twelve Improvement Notices were issued.

Table 17 Prosecutions brought by HM Railway Inspectorate heard during 1994/95

Defendant	Date of offence and location	Legislation breached	Penalty imposed	Nature of incident leading to offence
Tilbury Douglas Ltd and	St John's Bridge Station 13/6/92	HSW Act S2(1) and S3(1) (Tilbury Douglas)	£25 000	Two employees killed during demolition of a railway bridge
British Railways Board		HSW Act S3(1) (British Railways Board)	£25 000	
Dyfed County Council	Llanboidy Level Crossing 27/4/94	HSW Act S3(1)	£3000	One passenger seriously injured when a train and a JCB at the crossing collided
British Railways Board	Bridge 29a Newcastle and Carlisle line at Bladon 4/10/94	HSW Act S2	£15 000	One employee injured when 11 kV cable struck during preparatory works for fence erection

338 Two INs related to inadequate railway fencing and two to failures to maintain public level crossings correctly. The other INs related mainly to inadequately maintained places of work or systems of work. Of the three PNs, one concerned poorly designed scaffolding beneath the Royal Border Bridge at Berwick, which was showing signs of collapse and another to a failure to take measures to detect buried services before excavation took place. The latter is a subject which has been the source of at least two prosecutions. Clear warnings have been issued by the Inspectorate that before any excavation takes place on railway land, there must be a documentary search, combined with questioning of any bodies likely to have services buried in the area, as well as a search with detecting equipment. A Railtrack Group Standard has now been issued on the subject.

Prosecutions

339 Three prosecutions brought by the Inspectorate were heard during the year, each alleging a breach of the HSW Act. One concerning the same incident involved a contractor and the British Railways Board and related to the collapse of a railway overbridge during demolition in which two of the contractor's employees were killed. Other prosecutions were of the British Railways Board and of a County Council. The County Council pleaded not guilty to a charge arising from a train accident at an Automatic Half Barrier Level Crossing when a tractor fitted with a back-acter and front loader (JCB) was being used for roadworks. It was obstructing the crossing without warning to the railway, and a train struck it. The cases are summarised in Table 17 and fines totalling £68 000 were imposed.

Personnel accident record

General

340 There is a temptation to look upon changes in the number of fatalities and injuries from year to year as indicative of deterioration or improvement in accident rates. The true position can only be seen from Figures 10, 11 and 12, which provide a ten-year picture. Broadly speaking, except for minor injuries, the current trends appear to be good, although the possible reasons for this were explored in last year's report. Even then, social changes and changes in railway organisation may result in some variation, while it is difficult to determine a figure which accurately defines the exposure of railway track workers to the hazards.

341 A total of 3672 staff accidents were reported. As described in Appendix 11, the reporting criteria for injuries to staff and contractors differ from those for injuries to the public. Most notifiable accidents to employees mean at the least absence from work for three days. The figure of 3672 is a reduction of 5% on last year's total.

342 In 1994/1995, there were nine worker fatalities compared to the previous year's lowest-ever of eight. Five resulted from train accidents, compared with none last year. One

involved a contractor on LUL who was electrocuted when he fell on a conductor rail and three involved track workers, one from LUL, who were struck by trains. Possibly a significant feature of two of these three movement accident deaths (the same as last year) is that they were all men on their own and separated from their fellow workers. One was a look-out. The total worker movement injury accidents reported to the Inspectorate was 204. In addition to the three fatalities, 186 of them were to train staff while on-board trains. Many of these were of trauma induced by accidents involving trespassers or suicides. Others were burns or scalds, injuries from train doors, or tripping or slipping on the train.

Train accidents

343 The details of the train accidents in which staff died are elsewhere in the report. In one accident at *Cowden* (RTSZ), Kent, two drivers and a guard, who was riding in one of the driving cabs, and two passengers, were killed in a head-on collision between two DEMUs on a single line. An Inquiry has been held into this accident and the report has been published. At *Branchton* (RTSc), Strathclyde a train driver and a passenger were killed when an EMU, derailed by concrete slabs placed on the line by vandals, struck a bridge abutment. Details are given in Chapter 13. At *Ais Gill* (RTEC), Cumbria a guard was killed when a DMU collided with another DMU that had been derailed on a landslide during torrential rain. An inquest is yet to be held (at the time of writing).

Movement accidents

344 The details of the accident which resulted in the death of an LUL employee when hit by a train at *West Hampstead* are in the LUL section of the report. Descriptions of the other two accidents are given below.

345 At *Trent South Junction* (RTMZ), Derbyshire on *12 December 1994* a look-out, who had given a warning of a train approaching to the gang with whom he was working, was apparently standing safely in the cess while the gang stood safely in a '10-foot' wideway. He must have moved or stumbled so that he was struck and killed by the train of which he had warned the gang, but because he was hidden from the gang while the train passed, no one saw what actually happened.

346 The other fatal movement accident was of a track chargeman who had been given the task of erecting temporary lighting ready for a weekend possession. He left the remainder of his gang and went onto the line near *Colwich* (RTWC), Staffordshire on *31 March 1995*. Because the tracks are on a curve and visibility is limited by an overbridge abutment, staff are briefed that they must have look-out protection when working in the area, although there is an adequate safe cess on the side from which the chargeman approached. Despite this, the man moved into the 'four-foot' and was seen attempting to jump clear at the last moment by the driver of a light locomotive travelling north, who could do nothing to prevent him being struck and killed.

Non-movement accidents

347 The sole non-movement fatality was that of a contractor working for LUL. Details of this accident are given in the LUL section of the report. The single largest number of accidents in this category in the year, as is usual, comes under the heading of slips, trips and falls at the same level. The total of 723 reported accidents is very close to that for 1993/94 and is again some 20% of all staff accidents. An IO is acting as the Inspectorate representative on an HSE-wide committee which is considering a strategy for a campaign to deal with this type of accident involving both staff and passengers.

348 As is usual, the large majority of reported accidents to staff and contractors are non-movement accidents. Most of those are equivalent to other industrial accidents with the exception of accidents involving contact with the live traction conductors. There were 16 of these including the fatality and 11 major injuries.

349 Manual handling accidents, while still a high proportion of non-movement accidents, continue to reduce in numbers and this year's total represents a reduction of some 20% on the figures for 1993/94.

Risk awareness programme

350 This comprises a series of eight video films which have been produced by Railtrack to heighten the awareness of staff to the causes, circumstances and prevention of accidents. They are well made and have been seen by most members of the Inspectorate.

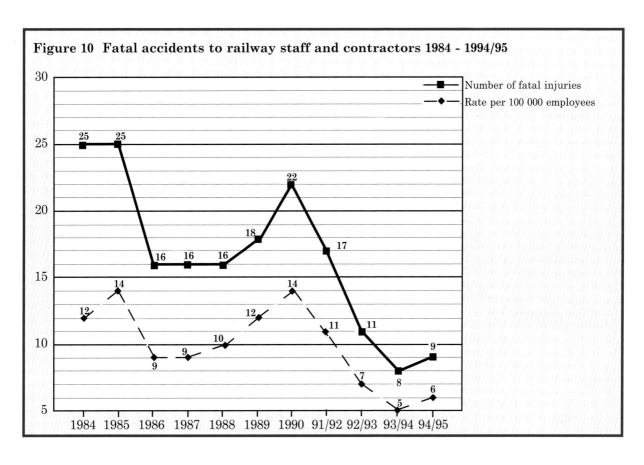

Figure 10 Fatal accidents to railway staff and contractors 1984 - 1994/95

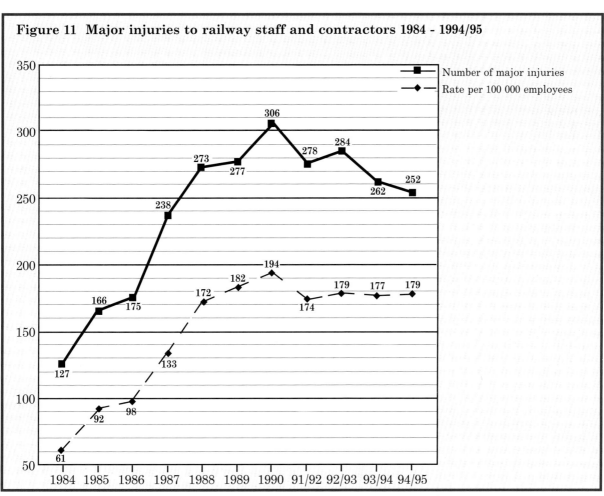

Figure 11 Major injuries to railway staff and contractors 1984 - 1994/95

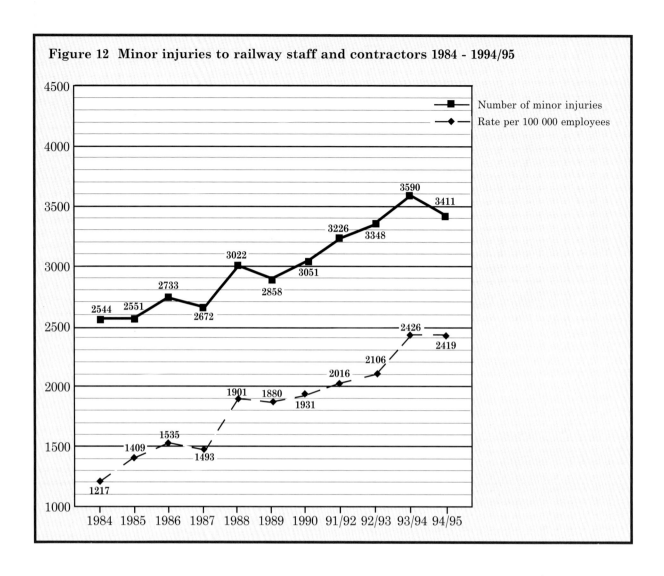

Figure 12 Minor injuries to railway staff and contractors 1984 - 1994/95

Number of minor injuries

Rate per 100 000 employees

Chapter 12 RESEARCH

Key facts

- Research continues to play an important part in the Inspectorate's programme of work
- Risk assessment techniques are increasingly being used to evaluate risks

Introduction

351 Research continues to be a priority activity for the Inspectorate and several projects which were underway or began in 1993/94 have continued this year. The following paragraphs describe progress on these individual projects and identify further work which is being undertaken.

Road user behaviour at level crossings

352 The Transport Research Laboratory (TRL) has undertaken a study of road user behaviour at signal-controlled level crossings. They reviewed earlier research, analysed the relevant statistics and interviewed 100 motorists observed driving through a crossing after the lights had started flashing. The report goes on to identify potential measures for reducing the likelihood of these incidents.

353 Three categories of driver behaviour were identified as being likely to cause accidents at level crossings:

(a) those who are unwilling to stop because they believe they have plenty of time to cross before the train arrives;

(b) those who are unable to stop because they are too close to the stop line at the onset of amber, or because someone is driving too closely behind;

(c) those who are unaware of the signals because they are inattentive or are distracted.

Analysis of accidents at level crossings

354 The most important conclusion to emerge from this part of the study is that, when judged by the standard set by conventional road junctions, level crossings are remarkably safe: the annual rate of injury accidents per level crossing is approximately one fiftieth of the rate at road junctions, and less than one two-hundredth of the rate at junctions controlled by automatic traffic signals. Although it is clear that significant numbers of drivers attempt to cross level crossings when being warned that a train is approaching, and some of them are in consequence involved in accidents, many more drivers fail to observe conventional traffic signals and become involved in accidents.

355 A model of the process which leads certain drivers to decide to cross illegally is suggested by this evidence. The model predicts that the number of illegal crossings could be reduced by increased enforcement and by making the risk of being struck by a train more obvious.

Survey of motorists

356 One hundred drivers were interviewed after being seen to cross level crossings when the red stop lights were flashing. The majority were regular users of level crossings. Crossing closure times were in general over-estimated, but most felt that the length of time was acceptable. Understanding of level crossing signals was on the whole less good than that of conventional road traffic signals.

Measures to improve safety

357 A review of the literature showed that there was relatively little to be learned from overseas experience in developing ways to elicit behaviour change by drivers. Traditional road safety practice in this country has a battery of measures at its disposal, most of which could in principle be applied to level crossings. Using the modern technology that is now available, a marked reduction in red light violations is a real possibility. However, to achieve gains in safety will be a more difficult proposition, in which long-term education and publicity as well as short-term enforcement will have a part to play.

Risk assessment of level crossings

358 In 1993 BRB commissioned a wide-ranging independent risk assessment into the relative safety of the different types of level crossings. This work identified that:

(a) in the majority of cases accidents occurred because of errors or violations by crossing users;

(b) unprotected crossings such as user worked or footpath crossings generally present the highest risk to regular users.

359 It also found that the risks to vehicle users of automatic crossings may also be higher where the following factors apply:

(a) high levels of utilisation;

(b) crossings where regular users travel in connection with work;

(c) road layouts with high approach speeds which encourage 'red running';

(d) crossings on straight roads with good visibility which enables zig-zag manoeuvres at half barriers;

(e) crossing layouts which make observation of warnings difficult, for example because of glare caused by low sun.

360 A computerised model has been developed to allow risk assessment for individual crossings, particularly to evaluate the relative effectiveness of different schemes aimed at improving safety performance and to allow resources and expenditure targeting for optimum effect.

361 Following this study and the TRL study, the Inspectorate has identified further work to examine specific options for reducing the risk to the users of level crossings. These include:

(a) further human behaviour studies;

(b) the use of alternative warning measures on the approach to or at level crossings;

(c) the identification of specific level crossings where reasonably practical measures can be introduced to reduce the risk to users.

Study of slip resistance of flooring

362 Following the work described in last year's report this project has been extended because of its wider importance for public safety.

363 The programme is examining the performance of shoe soles made from different materials on floor surfaces having different characteristics such as surface roughness and hardness. Results of the study are not yet available.

Platform safety

364 After the project was announced last year, there has been a survey of accidents since 1984 involving step gap/heights between platforms and trains. This survey identified 61 accidents resulting from boarding/alighting activities. The accident reports and the relevant platform/ train parameters were studied. This data is currently being analysed to identify whether a correlation exists between the incidents and the stepping distances involved.

Use of escalators in an emergency

365 This project began last year and has now been completed. It has examined the potential for the remote reversal of escalators to effect the rapid evacuation of passengers, for example in the event of fire. The work involved the modelling of passenger response to measured accelerations and the results were inconclusive. It showed for instance that passengers could fall as a result of escalators stopping in service, but that passengers are also known to fall for other reasons. Cascade falls, where more than one passenger falls, have also occurred but these involve few people.

366 Measurements also predicted that passengers would experience lower decelerations when escalators are heavily loaded, thereby reducing the likelihood of passengers falling on heavily loaded escalators. Further work would therefore be needed to support the use of escalators for this purpose.

Track layout risk assessment

367 This jointly sponsored BR (Railtrack) and HMRI risk assessment project was announced in last year's report. The project has been an important one and has involved close collaboration between HMRI and Railtrack personnel with the consultants, A D Little.

368 The first stage was to undertake an analysis of hazards which could arise at a layout. These were then analysed and marked to categorise their individual contributions to the overall risk at specific locations. A method has been derived for quantifying the likelihood of incidents, and assessments of the risk at specific layouts have been made. The method is

currently being tested to examine its sensitivity to different parameters, for example, the likelihood of a SPAD, and its robustness compared with historical incident data. This validation of the method is continuing and, given successful completion, the technique will be valuable, both in designing new layouts and in assessing relative risk of existing track layouts and the possible need to reduce the risk at specific locations.

369 HMRI are continuing to collaborate closely with Railtrack in validating and applying the model to real-life situations to identify locations where further risk reduction measures will be reasonably practicable.

Risk to the public at unsupervised stations

370 This project has been commissioned following a tragic accident involving the death of a young child who made contact with an electrified third rail while playing with friends at an unsupervised station.

371 The accident raised questions about access and security of stations and whether effective and practicable means exist for preventing or restricting access to them.

372 Work is currently underway to:

(a) determine the extent and nature of trespass activities which use stations as the point of access;

(b) identify and detail relevant accident data;

(c) clarify stations' operating procedures;

(d) specify current control measures;

(e) identify additional reasonably practicable control measures to reduce the risk.

Discussion

373 It will be apparent that the research projects described above are increasingly using the techniques of risk assessment. This structured approach to the identification, analysis and assessment of hazards is a powerful tool when used constructively, particularly in clarifying the relative significance of different hazards and in prioritising actions for reducing the risks from a variety of hazards.

374 The approach does however need to be applied sensibly. It can be an important aid to decision making, but it can also be misused. For example, the technique is sometimes used to justify a radical departure from established good practice by demonstrating that the cost of a measure is disproportionate to the safety benefit provided. Such proposals need to be very critically examined to demonstrate the validity of the proposal to ensure that safety is being maintained and risks are being reduced so far as is reasonably practicable.

375 A number of other projects are currently being considered, including a jointly sponsored study involving HMRI/Railtrack/BR into the causes of the observed phenomenon that employees appear more prone than average to personal injury and human error approximately 2 to 3 hours after commencing work. The work will be offered for tender and will take 1.5 to 2 years to complete.

376 In addition to sponsoring research directly, HMRI seeks to increasingly cosponsor projects with railway operators and others in the railway industry. HMRI considers it very important that the industry, albeit in the radically restructured form which is currently emerging, continues to invest in and support relevant safety research. There is clearly a danger that the current research momentum within the railway sector could be threatened by the fragmentation of the industry and HMRI will be seeking to encourage the continuing involvement and participation of newly created railway companies in the field of research.

377 If this is to be successful, the co-operation of all parties will be necessary and it is hoped that an industry-led safety research programme will be maintained during this period of great change in the railway industry.

Chapter 13 VANDALISM

Key facts

- Driver and passenger killed in Branchton derailment due to vandalism
- There were 228 acts of vandalism this year compared with 289 in 1993/94 (a reduction of 61)
- Slight increase of arson incidents on trains

378 As briefly mentioned in last year's report, two people, a passenger and the train driver, died as the result of the derailment of the 22.45 Wemyss Bay to Glasgow Central EMU passenger train at *Branchton*, Strathclyde, on *25 June 1994*. This was caused by deliberate obstruction of the line by two teenage boys. Strathclyde Police, with the help of their British Transport Police colleagues, soon arrested the culprits and they were duly found guilty of culpable homicide and sentenced to 15 years imprisonment.

379 While such derailment is fortunately rare, the attempts are all too common. Two further substantial obstructions were placed on Scottish lines on 26 June, one in Strathclyde for which someone is now serving a one-year prison sentence, the other was in Lothian where a hearing is awaited. In the year under review, trains are reported to have run into 131 obstructions placed maliciously, causing six derailments. It is worth noting, however, that this total is a reduction of 60 over the number reported in 1993/94.

380 It is not only the national railway network that suffers from the attentions of vandals. Three of the six derailments were of trains on narrow gauge minor railways

381 Overhead line equipment still exerts a fascination for vandals in spite of the serious risk it poses to those who interfere with it. Two such incidents are related in Chapter 6.

382 Table 18 shows a further increase in arson attacks on trains.

383 There are many manifestations of vandalism beside the wrecking of trains.

Table 18 Train accidents caused by vandalism

	91/92	92/93	93/94	94/95
Collision	2	3	3	1
Derailment	2	2	1	6
Running into obstructions	122	196	191	131
Fires in trains	36	63	85	89
Others	1	2	9	1
Total	**163**	**266**	**289**	**228**

The deliberate derailment of the passenger train at Branchton on 25 June 1994, causing damage to the front section of the leading coach

Buildings and rolling stock are defaced with paint and unattended facilities are destroyed. London Underground spends some £2 million a year on cleaning paint damage alone.

384 A gate damaged by vandals beside the main line near *Nuneaton*, Warwickshire, enabled 12 horses to stray onto the railway, on *9 January 1995*. Five of them were killed when they were struck by a Manchester to London express passenger train.

APPENDIX 1

Accidents and failures, numbers of staff and operating statistics

	Train accidents	Failures of rolling stock and permanent way	Railway staff	Train miles operated				Passenger journeys (including season tickets)		Passenger miles (estimate)	
				Total	Railtrack/BR		Metropolitan Railways*	Railtrack/ BR	Metropolitan Railways*	Railtrack/ BR	Metropolitan Railways*
					Passenger	Freight					
	Number		Thousands	Million train miles				Millions		Millions	
1990	1283	1776	158	302	231	37†	34	762	783	20624	3882
1991/92	960	1609	160	313	219	54†	40	762	825	19920	4140
1992/93	1152	1862	159	311	228	37†	46	769	787	19709	3893
1993/94	977	1777	148	304	217	47†	40	740	803	18841	3892
1994/95	**907**	**1787**	**141**	**304**	**212**	**47†**	**45**	**735**	**848**	**17806**	**4112**

* Metropolitan Railways include Tyne & Wear Metro, London Underground Limited, Strathclyde Glasgow Underground Railways, Docklands Light Railway, Blackpool Transport Services, Manchester Metro, South Yorkshire Supertram Ltd, Euro Tunnel UK and European Passenger Services

† Includes empty coaching stock

APPENDIX 2

Casualties in all accidents

	Killed						Major injuries						Minor injuries					
	1994/95	1993/94	1992/93	1991/92	1991	1990	**1994/95**	1993/94	1992/93	1991/92	1991	1990	**1994/95**	1993/94	1992/93	1991/92	1991	1990
All accidents																		
Total	**42**	40	39	68	16	78	**485**	484	536	495	172	550	**10161**	10379	9699	9 156	2298	9500
Passengers	17	16	18	31	8	37	204	205	238	192	92	224	6586	6606	6125	5788	1477	6240
Railway staff*	9	8	11	17	5	22	252	262	284	278	76	306	3411	3590	3348	3226	798	3051
Other persons†	16	16	10	20	3	19	29	17	14	25	4	20	164	183	226	142	23	209
Train accidents																		
Total	**12**	6	5	11	3	4	**24**	11	13	30	38	22	**272**	235	140	361	531	221
Passengers	3	-	-	2	2	-	11	5	3	18	34	13	179	129	63	289	515	144
Railway staff*	5	-	1	2	-	1	8	4	5	6	4	6	75	91	69	59	14	67
Other persons†	4	6	4	7	1	3	5	2	5	6	-	3	18	15	8	13	2	10
Movement accidents																		
Total	**27**	26	27	49	13	69	**73**	66	116	113	28	157	**2344**	2307	2442	2247	384	2620
Passengers	12	14	16	28	6	35	58	41	79	73	19	107	2157	2168	2335	2181	375	2551
Railway staff*	3	3	5	9	5	19	14	23	34	39	8	48	187	134	106	65	9	68
Other persons†	12	9	6	12	2	15	1	2	3	1	1	2	-	5	1	1	-	1
Non-movement accidents																		
Total	**3**	8	7	8	-	5	**388**	407	407	352	106	371	**7545**	7837	7117	6548	1383	6659
Passengers	2	2	2	1	-	2	135	159	156	101	39	104	4250	4309	3727	3318	587	3545
Railway staff*	1	5	5	6	-	2	230	235	245	233	64	252	3149	3365	3173	3102	775	2916
Other persons†	-	1	-	1	-	1	23	13	6	18	3	15	146	163	217	128	21	198

* Railway staff includes contractors' staff

† Excluding trespassers, suicides and attempted suicides

Fatal accident figures for 1990 - 1993/94 have been revised following notification of Coroners' findings for inquests which were outstanding at the time the previous statistics were prepared

The figures for 1991 cover 1 January 1991 - 31 March 1991

Table 1   Death or injury rate: passengers (Repeated for comparison)

Year	Train accidents *per billion passenger miles*			Movement accidents *per billion passenger miles*			Non-movement accidents *per billion passenger journeys*		
	Killed	Major	Minor	Killed	Major	Minor	Killed	Major	Minor
1989	0.24	1.58	11.03	1.01	3.93	105.40	1.25	82.55	2687
1990	-	0.53	5.88	1.43	4.37	104.10	1.29	67.31	2294
1991/92	0.08	0.75	12.01	1.16	3.03	90.65	0.63	63.64	2091
1992/93	-	0.13	2.67	0.68	3.35	98.93	1.29	100.26	2395
1993/94	-	0.22	5.67	0.62	1.80	95.37	1.30	103.05	2793
1994/95	0.14	0.50	8.17	0.55	2.65	98.41	1.26	85.28	2685

APPENDIX 3

Train accidents and failures of rolling stock and permanent way

		All railways		1994/95			
		1993/94	1994/95	Railtrack/BR	LUL	Trams	Other
Index	**Train accidents total**	977	**907**	**806**	**26**	**51**	**24**
	Total collisions	135	**125**	**118**	**3**	**3**	**1**
	Collisions between:						
*1	Passenger trains or parts thereof	9	7	4	-	3	-
*2	Passenger trains and freight trains or light locomotives	5	11	10	-	-	1
*3	Freight trains, light locomotives or other moving vehicles**	12 (2)	6 (1)	5 (1)	1 (-)	- (-)	- (-)
4	Trains and vehicles standing foul of line**	- (-)	- (-)	- (-)	- (-)	- (-)	- (-)
*5	Trains and buffer stops or vehicles standing at buffer stops**	31 (-)	21 (-)	20 (-)	1 (-)	- (-)	- (-)
6	Trains and projections from other trains or vehicles on parallel lines †	78 (59)	80 (71)	79 (71)	1 (-)	- (-)	- (-)
	Total derailments	113	**149**	**114**	**8**	**16**	**11**
	Derailments:						
*7	of passenger trains	29	28	9	1	12	6
*8	of freight trains**	84 (26)	121 (42)	105 (42)	7 (-)	4 (-)	5 (-)
	Total running into obstructions	445	**397**	**348**	**12**	**30**	**7**
9	Trains running into:						
	(a) gates or vehicles or animals at level crossings	49	33	28	-	-	5
	(b) animals on the line	78	89	89	-	-	-
	(c) other obstacles	318	275	231	12	30	2
	Total fires on trains	247	**217**	**207**	**3**	**2**	**5**
10	Fires in trains:						
	(a) passenger trains	217	169	160	3	2	4
	(b) freight trains	30	48	47	-	-	1
	Total other accidents†	37 (28)	**19 (17)**	**19 (17)**	**- (-)**	**- (-)**	**- (-)**
11	Other accidents†	37 (28)	19 (17)	19 (17)	- (-)	- (-)	- (-)
	Failures of rolling stock and permanent way etc total	1777	**1787**	**1683**	**73**	**8**	**23**
	Total for rolling stock	277	**271**	**235**	**25**	**5**	**6**
12	Failure of locomotives and multiple unit trains:						
	(a) diesel††	45 (3)	35 (8)	35 (8)	- (-)	- (-)	- (-)
	(b) electric††	117 (-)	135 (33)	107 (25)	22 (8)	3 (-)	3 (-)
	(c) steam	-	-	-	-	-	-
13	General failures of rolling stock (excluding indices 14,15 and 16)	23	16	13	-	2	1
14	Failures of wheels or tyres	25	25	24	1	-	-
15	Failures of axles	20	15	15	-	-	-
16	Failure of coupling apparatus:						
	(a) passenger	43	44	40	2	-	2
	(b) freight	4	1	1	-	-	-
	Total for permanent way and structures	1500	**1516**	**1448**	**48**	**3**	**17**
17	Failure of structures:						
	(a) tunnels, bridges, viaducts, culverts etc	54	64	54	9	1	-
	(b) damage to bridges etc by motor vehicles & ships	74	74	67	6	-	1
18	Failure of track:						
	(a) broken rails	743	686	656	21	1	8
	(b) track buckles	25	46	46	-	-	-
19	Flooding of permanent way, slips in cuttings etc	210	283	277	4	-	2
20	Fires at passenger stations, signal-boxes etc	118	88	80	8	-	-
21	Failures of overhead line equipment	50	38	32	-	1	5
22	Miscellaneous failures	226	237	236	-	-	1

Note: The index numbers correlate with those at Appendix 5

*   Accidents considered significant when occuring on or affecting passenger lines

†   Figures marked in brackets denote the number of open door collisions included in each total

**   Figures marked in brackets denote the number of accidents which occurred on freight only lines or lines in the possession of the engineer included in each total

††   Figures marked in brackets denote the number of powered door failures included in each total not attributed to operator error or malicious action

APPENDIX 4

Train accidents in 1994/95: analysis by primary causes

	Total	Collisions	Derailments	Running into obstructions	Fires in trains	Other accidents
Total	907	125	149	397	217	19
Staff error total	142	42	53	38	8	1
Train crews (Including guards):						
(a) passing signals at danger	8	2	4	1	-	1
(b) other irregularities or want of care:						
(i) drivers	52	31	14	7	-	-
(ii) guards	2	-	1	-	1	-
(iii) drivers and guards	18	6	8	2	2	-
Signalmen:						
(a) irregular block working	-	-	-	-	-	-
(b) other irregularities or want of care	4	-	3	1	-	-
Other staff:						
(a) in traffic departments	12	1	11	-	-	-
(b) in other departments	37	1	6	25	5	-
Train crews and signalmen	-	-	-	-	-	-
Train crews and other staff	1	-	1	-	-	-
Signalmen and other staff	-	-	-	-	-	-
Faulty loading	8	1	5	2	-	-
Technical defects total	209	8	77	13	111	-
Locomotives and multiple units	107	2	9	-	96	-
Vehicles	24	4	6	-	14	-
Track	61	1	53	7	-	-
Signalling apparatus	4	-	1	3	-	-
Overhead line equipment	1	-	-	1	-	-
Other structures	8	-	5	2	1	-
Combined defects	-	-	-	-	-	-
Traction and braking shocks	4	1	3	-	-	-
Other causes total	556	75	19	346	98	18
Snow, landslides, floods etc	49	2	2	44	1	-
Animals on line	83	-	-	83	-	-
Irresponsibility of the public:						
(a) irregular opening of doors	88	71	-	-	-	17
(b) at level crossings	27	-	-	27	-	-
(c) malicious	228	1	6	131	89	1
(d) other	61	-	1	57	3	-
Miscellaneous and cause not determined	20	1	10	4	5	-

APPENDIX 5

Casualties in train accidents in 1994/95: analysis by type of accident

Index		Killed				Major injuries				Minor injuries			
		Total	Passengers	Railway staff†	Other persons	Total	Passengers	Railway staff†	Other persons	Total	Passengers	Railway staff†	Other persons
	Total	**12**	**3**	**5**	**4**	**24**	**11**	**8**	**5**	**272**	**179**	**75**	**18**
Index	**Total from collisions**	**6**	**2**	**4**	-	**12**	**7**	**5**	-	**193**	**162**	**31**	-
*1	Collisions between: Passenger trains or parts thereof	6	2	4	-	5	3	2	-	73	66	7	-
*2	Passenger trains and freight trains or light locomotives	-	-	-	-	6	4	2	-	95	84	11	-
*3	Freight trains, light locomotives or other moving vehicles	-	-	-	-	-	-	-	-	2	-	2	-
4	Trains and vehicles standing foul of the line	-	-	-	-	-	-	-	-	-	-	-	-
*5	Trains and buffer stops or vehicles standing at buffer stops	-	-	-	-	1	-	1	-	23	12	11	-
6	Trains and projections from other trains or vehicles on parallel lines	-	-	-	-	-	-	-	-	-	-	-	-
	Total from derailments	**2**	**1**	**1**	-	**1**	-	**1**	-	**6**	**3**	**3**	-
*7	Derailments of passenger trains	2	1	1	-	-	-	-	-	4	3	1	-
*8	Derailments of freight trains	-	-	-	-	1	-	1	-	2	-	2	-
	Total from running into obstructions	**4**	-	-	**4**	**10**	**4**	**1**	**5**	**51**	**14**	**19**	**18**
9	Trains running into obstructions:												
	(a) at level crossings	3	-	-	3	4	1	1	2	25	5	8	12
	(b) and (c) elsewhere**	1	-	-	1	6	3	-	3	26	9	11	6
	Total from fires in trains	-	-	-	-	**1**	-	**1**	-	**21**	-	**21**	-
10	Fires in trains:												
	(a) passenger trains	-	-	-	-	1	-	1	-	2	-	2	-
	(b) freight trains	-	-	-	-	-	-	-	-	19	-	19	-
	Total from other accidents	-	-	-	-	-	-	-	-	**1**	-	**1**	-
11	Other accidents	-	-	-	-	-	-	-	-	1	-	1	-

*   Accidents considered significant when occurring on or affecting passenger lines
†   Railway staff includes contractors' staff
** See Appendix 3 for details

APPENDIX 6

Casualties in movement accidents in 1994/95: analysis by type of accident

Index		Total	Killed	Major injuries	Minor injuries
Index	**Passengers total**	**2227**	**12**	**58**	**2157**
1	Entering or alighting from trains	693	1	28	664
2	Falling off platforms and being struck or run over by train	21	3	7	11
3	Crossing the lines at stations	8	1	4	3
4	Opening or closing of carriage doors	583	-	7	576
5	Falling out of carriages during the running of trains	19	6	4	9
6	Other accidents	903	1	8	894
	Railway staff * total	**204**	**3**	**14**	**187**
	Shunting accidents:	-	-	-	-
1	Getting on or off, or falling off, moving locomotive wagons	-	-	-	-
2	Coming into contact with vehicles or fixed lineside objects when riding on locomotives etc	-	-	-	-
3	Staff on train involved in a collision in sidings	2	-	1	1
4	Being caught between vehicles while coupling or uncoupling	-	-	-	-
5	Struck or caught between vehicles when walking on the line	1	-	-	1
6	Miscellaneous	1	-	1	-
	Accidents during the running of trains:				
7	Getting on or off, or falling from, locomotives, wagons etc	6	-	2	4
8	Coming into contact with fixed lineside objects when riding on trains etc	-	-	-	-
9	Train staff while on board train	186	-	10	176
10	Miscellaneous	-	-	-	-
	Accidents to staff working on or about the track:				
11	Struck by train etc when acting as lookoutman or handsignalman	-	-	-	-
12	Struck by train etc when working on or about the track	4	3	-	1
13	Struck by train etc when authorised to walk on the track	-	-	-	-
14	Struck by flying objects or out-of-gauge parts of a train	-	-	-	-
15	Miscellaneous	-	-	-	-
	Other movement accidents:				
16	Struck by train etc when required to cross the line on duty	-	-	-	-
17	Struck by train etc when not required to walk on the track (including failure to use an authorised route)	-	-	-	-
18	Through movement of vehicles at which men were engaged	-	-	-	-
19	Miscellaneous	4	-	-	4
	Other persons † total	**13**	**12**	**1**	**-**
1	At level crossings	11	10	1	-
2	On business at stations or sidings	-	-	-	-
3	Miscellaneous	2	2	-	-

* Railway staff total includes contractors' staff
† Excluding trespassers, suicides and attempted suicides

APPENDIX 7

Casualties in non-movement accidents in 1994/95: analysis by type of accident

Index		Total	Killed	Major injuries	Minor injuries
	Passengers total	**4387**	**2**	**135**	**4250**
1	Ascending or descending steps and escalators at stations	1731	-	40	1691
2	Being struck by barrows, falling over packages etc	126	-	1	125
3	Falling from platform onto line	78	-	5	73
4	Electric shock on electrified railways	2	1	1	-
5	Slips, trips and falls	1460	1	77	1382
6	Other accidents	990	-	11	979
	Railway staff * total	**3380**	**1**	**230**	**3149**
1	Contact with or being trapped by moving machinery or material being machined	30	-	6	24
2	Struck by moving, including flying or falling object, other than rails	236	-	18	218
3	Struck by moving vehicle (other than rail vehicle)	21	-	2	19
4	Struck against something fixed or stationary	186	-	6	180
5	Injured while handling, lifting or carrying other than rails	442	-	3	439
6	Fall through a height of more than 2 metres	18	-	11	7
7	Fall through a height of 2 metres or less	185	-	23	162
8	Fall from a stationary rail vehicle	74	-	3	71
9	Slip, trip or fall on the same level	723	-	84	639
10	Trapped by something collapsing or overturning	32	-	-	32
11	Burnt or scalded other than by chemical or electrical agents	47	-	3	44
12	Using power-driven hand tools	32	-	3	29
13	Using unpowered hand tools	92	-	3	89
14	Handling rails by manual or mechanical means	77	-	2	75
15	Electric shock or burns from plant or equipment	12	-	10	2
16	Electric shock or burns from live rail on electrified lines	11	1	8	2
17	Electric shock or burns from overhead electrification equipment	5	-	3	2
18	Harmed by lack of oxygen (eg drowning/asphyxiation)	-	-	-	-
19	Injured by explosion	1	-	1	-
20	Contact with or exposure to harmful substance	30	-	9	21
21	Assaulted while on duty	323	-	9	314
22	Miscellaneous	803	-	23	780
	Other persons † total	**169**	**-**	**23**	**146**
1	On business	97	-	23	74
2	Miscellaneous	72	-	-	72

* Railway staff include contractors and post office staff handling mail
† Excluding trespassers, suicides and attempted suicides

APPENDIX 8

Casualties to trespassers, suicides and attempted suicides in 1994/95

	Total		Killed		Major injuries		Minor injuries	
Movement accidents total	**277**	**(6)**	**232**	**(4)**	**29**	**(1)**	**16**	**(1)**
Trespassers	163	(6)	118	(4)	29	(1)	16	(1)
Suicides and attempted suicides	114	(-)	114	(-)	-	(-)	-	(-)
Non-movement accidents total	**62**	**(14)**	**22**	**(2)**	**32**	**(8)**	**8**	**(4)**
Trespassers								
(a) electric shock on electrified railways								
(i) conductor rail system	12	(4)	6	(1)	6	(3)	-	(-)
(ii) OLE system	12	(4)	3	(-)	7	(3)	2	(1)
(b) other causes	31	(6)	7	(1)	19	(2)	5	(3)
Suicides and attempted suicides	7	(-)	6	(-)	-	(-)	1	(-)
Totals in all accidents	**339**	**(20)**	**254**	**(6)**	**61**	**(9)**	**24**	**(5)**

Note: The figures in brackets denote the number of children under the age of 16 years included in each total

APPENDIX 8a

Fatal accidents to trespassers and suicides 1990 - 1994/95

	1994/95		1993/94		1992/93		1991/92		1991*		1990	
Trespassers	134	(6)	121	(7)	132	(5)	150	(7)	30	(-)	154	(14)
Suicides	120	(-)	141	(1)	132	(-)	150	(1)	33	(2)	157	(-)
Total	**254**	**(6)**	**262**	**(8)**	**264**	**(5)**	**300**	**(8)**	**63**	**(2)**	**311**	**(14)**

Note: The figures in brackets denote the number of children under the age of 16 years included in the total

Figures for 1990 - 1993/94 have been revised following notification of Coroners' findings for inquests which were outstanding at the time the previous statistics were prepared

* The figures for 1991 cover the period 1 January 1991 - 31 March 1991

ABBREVIATIONS

The following abbreviations have been used:

ABCL	automatic barrier crossing, locally monitored
ac	alternating current
ACIO	Assistant Chief Inspecting Officer (of Railways)
AHB	automatic half barrier
AIR	Association of Independent Railways
AOCL	automatic open crossing, locally monitored
AOCR	automatic open crossing, remotely monitored
ARPS	Association of Railway Preservation Societies
ASLEF	Associated Society of Locomotive Engineers and Firemen
ATC	automatic train control
ATO	automatic train operation
ATP	automatic train protection
AWS	automatic warning system
BR	British Rail
BRB	British Railways Board
BREL	British Rail Engineering Limited
BRUTE	British Rail Universal Trolley Equipment
BTP	British Transport Police
BTS	Blackpool Transport Services
CCTV	closed-circuit television
COSHH	Control of Substances Hazardous to Health Regulations 1994
CSDE	correct side door enable
CSR	cab secure radio
CWR	continous welded rail
dc	direct current
DCIO	Deputy Chief Inspecting Officer (of Railways)
DEMU	diesel-electric multiple unit (passenger train unless otherwise described)
DIAS	Directorate of Information and Advisory Services (of HSE)
DLR	Docklands Light Railway
DMU	diesel multiple unit (passenger train unless otherwise described)
DO	dangerous occurrences
DOT	Department of Transport
EC	European Community
ECS	empty coaching stock (train)
EMU	electric multiple unit (passenger train unless otherwise described)
EPS	European Passenger Services
ETUK	Euro Tunnel UK
FOD	Field Operations Division (of HSE)
FP	footpath (level crossing)
GLW	gross laden weight
GM	Strathclyde Glasgow Underground Railway
GMML	Greater Manchester Metro Limited
HMFI	Her Majesty's Factory Inspectorate
HMRI	Her Majesty's Railway Inspectorate
HSC	Health and Safety Commission
HSE	Health and Safety Executive
HST	High-speed train
HSW Act	Health and Safety at Work etc Act 1974
ICEC	East Coast Train Operating Unit
ICGW	Great Western Train Operating Unit
ICMX	Cross-country Train Operating Unit
ICWC	West Coast Train Operating Unit
IECC	integrated electronic control centre
ILWS	inductive loop warning system
IN	Improvement Notice
IO	Inspecting Officer (of Railways)
ISRS	International Safety Rating System
kV	kilovolt
LFDCA	London Fire and Civil Defence Authority
LRT	light rapid transit
LRV	light rail vehicle
LUL	London Underground Limited
MCB	manually controlled barrier (operated by a railway employee)
MG	manual gate (operated by a railway employee including those operated by trainmen)
MU	multiple unit (train)

MWL	miniature warning light
NIR	Northern Ireland Railways
NLTS	London, Tilbury and Southend Train Operating Unit
NRN	National Railway Network
NSCh	Chiltern Lines Train Operating Unit
NSE	Network Southeast
NSGE	Great Eastern Train Operating Unit
NSSC	Network South Central Train Operating Unit
NSSE	South Eastern Train Operating Unit
NSSW	South West Trains Train Operating Unit
NSTh	Thames Trains Train Operating Unit
NSTL	Thameslink Train Operating Unit
NWAN	West Anglia and Great Northern Train Operating Unit
OC	open crossing
OLC	occupation level crossing (private)
OLE	overhead line equipment
OPO	one person operated
ORV	occupant of road vehicle
PICOP	person in charge of possession
PICOW	person in charge of works
PIO	Principal Inspecting Officer (of Railways)
PLC	public level crossing
PN	Prohibition Notice
RAP	remedial action projects
RAPRA	Rubber and Plastics Research Association
RCH	Railway Clearing House
RfD	Railfreight Distribution
RH & DR	Romney, Hythe and Dymchurch Light Railway
RI	Railway Inspectorate
RIAC	Railway Industry Advisory Committee
RIDDOR	Reporting of Injuries, Diseases and Dangerous Occurrences Regulations
RMT	National Union of Rail, Maritime and Transport Workers
RRC	Central Train Operating Unit
RRNE	North East Train Operating Unit
RRSc	Scotrail Train Operating Unit
RRNW	North West Train Operating Unit
RSCW	Railway (Safety Critical Work) Regulations 1994
RSWW	South West and Wales Train Operating Unit
RTEA	Railtrack East Anglia Zone
RTEC	Railtrack East Coast Main Line Zone
RTGW	Railtrack Great Western Zone
RTMZ	Railtrack Midlands Zone
RTNE	Railtrack North East Zone
RTNW	Railtrack North West Zone
RTSc	Railtrack Scotland Zone
RTSZ	Railtrack South Zone
RTSW	Railtrack South West Zone
RTWC	Railtrack West Coast Main Line Zone
S&C	switches & crossings
S&T	signal & telecommunications
SMS	safety management system
SoS	Secretary of State (for Transport)
SPAD	signal passed at danger
SSI	solid state interlocking
SYSL	South Yorkshire Supertram Limited
T&W	Tyne and Wear Metro
TC	track circuit
TCA	track circuit actuator
TCAID	track circuit actuator interference detector
TLF	trainload freight
TML	Transmanche Link
TOU	Train operating unit
TRL	Transport Research Laboratory
TSWG	Track Safety Working Group
UWC	user worked crossing with either gates or lifting barriers not manned by a railway employee. (T) denotes telephone provided
VDU	visual display unit
W&L	Welshpool & Llanfair Light Railway
WSF	wrong side failure

APPENDIX 10

Electrified route mileages

	RT	LUL	DLR	BTS	GMML	SYSL	GM	T & W	EPS	ETUK	Total
Route mileage	10780	245.4	13.67	11.1	19.6	34.5	6.55	37.95	-	56.55	11205.32
Track mileage without sidings	20056	518.1	24.85	11.1	19.1	33.5	13.1	73.04	1	46.7	20796.49
ac overhead	1860	-	-	-	-	-	-	-	-	0.78	1860.78
dc overhead	-	-	-	11.1	19.6	34.5	-	37.95	-	56.55	159.7
dc conductor rail	1277	245.4	29.83	-	-	-	15.27	-	-	-	1567.5

Key:

RT	Railtrack
LUL	London Underground Limited
DLR	Docklands Light Railway
BTS	Blackpool Transport Services
GMML	Greater Manchester Metro Limited
SYSL	South Yorkshire Supertram Limited
GM	Strathclyde Glasgow Underground Railway
T&W	Tyne and Wear Metro
EPS	European Passenger Services
ETUK	Euro Tunnel UK

REGULATORY PROCEDURES

1   The year 1994/95 saw the introduction of the four key pieces of legislation which were made necessary by the policy of privatising the railways.

Railways and Other Transport Systems (Approval of Works, Plant and Equipment) Regulations 1994
Came into force 5 April 1994

Railways (Safety Case) Regulations 1994
Came into force 28 February 1994 but applicable in practice from 1 April 1994

Railways (Safety Critical Work) Regulations 1994
Came into force 1 April 1994

Carriage of Dangerous Goods by Rail Regulations 1994
Came into force 1 April 1994

2   The actions of the Railway Inspectorate to ensure that these various Regulations are implemented by the railways are described elsewhere in this report. The earlier regulatory Acts and secondary legislation remained largely unchanged, and the various functions etc under them are set out in the following paragraphs.

Inspection

3   Under the Transport and Works Act 1992, no railway, part of a railway, any fixed works, or electric traction may be brought into use for passenger traffic without the approval of the Secretary of State. Large installations as well as new methods of signalling are also subject to the Secretary of State's approval. Before this is given, or as a condition, the works are inspected, and the inspecting officer may require any additions or alterations which he may consider necessary for the safety of the public and railway staff. New level crossings as well as alterations in the methods of protection at existing level crossings by orders made under the British Transport Commission Act 1957, the Transport Act 1968, or the Level Crossings Act 1983, are also subject to the Secretary of State's approval and are inspected prior to approval being given.

Safety rules and regulations

4   In accordance with the Regulation of Railways Act 1889, orders were made requiring the railways to adopt the block system on passenger lines, to provide interlocking between points and signals on such lines, and to equip all passenger trains with a continuous brake. Also, under the Regulation of Railways Act 1868, means of passenger communication must be provided on all trains running over 20 miles without a stop. These obligations are still in force. As part of the supervision exercised under inspection procedure, the Secretary of State's present functions under the 1889 Act are confined to granting exemptions from the orders in respect of block working where special conditions prevail.

5   The Railway Employment (Prevention of Accidents) Act 1900 empowers the Secretary of State to make rules with the object of reducing or removing the dangers and risks incidental to railway service. Certain rules on matters specified in the Act were made in 1902 and 1911.

6   The Secretary of State had no jurisdiction over the construction of rolling stock (except where specifically provided in the enabling legislation), the maintenance of permanent way or signalling equipment, or the qualifications of operating staff.

Accidents

7   Under the Regulation of Railways Act 1871, and the Railway Employment (Prevention of Accidents) Act 1900, all accidents to trains on statutory railways and all those involving death or injury on railway premises are reported to the Secretary of State under the Railways (Notice of Accidents) Order 1986 (SI No 2187), which came into force on 1 January 1987. The Secretary of State is empowered by these Acts to order an inquiry into any of the accidents so reported, and this is done when circumstances warrant it. Reports of all accident inquiries conducted under the 1871 Act are made public under the terms of the Act.

8   The Notice of Accidents Order requires all accidents to passengers or other persons to be

reported, however slight their injuries may be, but accidents to railway staff or contractors' employees need only be reported when the injuries are such as to cause absence from ordinary work for more than three days. Personal injuries are classed as 'major' or 'minor'. The former is defined as: 'fractures other than a bone in the hand or foot; amputation of a hand or foot; amputation of a finger, thumb or toe; burns or electric shock requiring hospital treatment; loss of sight of an eye; loss of consciousness from lack of oxygen; decompression sickness; acute illness from exposure to a pathogen; admission into a hospital for treatment for more than 24 hours'. Any person who is known to have died from injuries before the date of this report is included as a fatality.

9   Under section 8 of the Act of 1871 the Secretary of State, if requested to do so by a coroner in England or Wales, appoints an assessor to assist at any inquest which may be held on a person killed in a railway accident. Assistance would similarly be afforded to a sheriff in Scotland if required under section 4 of the Fatal Accidents and Sudden Deaths Inquiry (Scotland) Act 1976. A report is required to be made public by the assessor so appointed.

10   The Reporting of Injuries, Diseases and Dangerous Occurrences Regulations 1985 (SI No 2023) came into effect from 1 April 1986. The latter Regulations redefined the term 'major injury'; the Railways (Notice of Accidents) Order 1986 incorporates the same definition so that statistics may be comparable between the railway and other industries. The Regulations made under the HSW Act apply to all work activities, not merely those in premises registered as factory premises or office, shop or railway premises, but accidents reportable under the railway legislation are not required to be reported separately. All railways are required to report dangerous occurrences as defined in the Regulations.

Agency Agreement

11   Under the HSW Act, the Department of Transport concluded an agreement with the Health and Safety Commission in respect of the application of the Act to railway workers. The agreement was effective from 1 April 1975 until 30 November 1990. The circumstances of the Railway Inspectorate's transfer to the Health and Safety Executive on 1 December 1990 were described in Chapter 1 of the 1990

report. From that date, a subsequent agreement came into effect between the Department and the Commission by means of which the Inspectorate performs several statutory functions on behalf of the Secretary of State for Transport. These include various duties under the railway regulatory acts, other railway and tramway legislation and the Channel Tunnel Act 1987.

Transport and Works Act 1992

12   The new order-making procedure established by this Act to replace private Bill procedure for authorising guided transport systems, inland waterways and works in the sea came into force on 1 January 1993. Other parts of the Act now in force include the new criminal offence of working on a railway or tramway while unfit through drink or drugs, provisions enabling the Secretary of State to sanction the stopping up or diversion of footpath or bridle-way level crossings in the interests of public safety and powers to require the provision of bridges or tunnels to replace non-vehicular level crossings.

APPENDIX 12a

TEXT OF A LETTER FROM THE CHAIRMAN OF THE HEALTH AND SAFETY COMMISSION, FRANK DAVIES, TO THE RT HON BRIAN MAWHINNEY, SECRETARY OF STATE FOR TRANSPORT

AUTOMATIC TRAIN PROTECTION

John MacGregor wrote to me last May requesting the Commission's advice, by the Autumn, on the report by British Rail (BR) on Automatic Train Protection (ATP) and on the issue of the values to be placed on a statistical life of safety investment purposes. I am pleased to respond.

In its consideration of the report, the Commission had very much in its mind the need to introduce systems to prevent accidents from signals passed at Danger, overspeeding or buffer stop collisions. These situations have the potential to cause catastrophic accidents. The recommendations of the Hidden Inquiry recognised this need. It is now five years since the report of the Hidden Inquiry was published and the Commission is concerned that action is seen to be taken on its recommendations.

We are aware that, concurrently with our consideration of the BR report, the Railway Inspectorate (RI) have been engaged in technical discussions with Railtrack (who, as national infrastructure controller, now has the prime responsibility for deciding on action to improve the safety of track and signalling). These discussions have not so far produced any firm indication from Railtrack of their intentions as regards reducing or preventing the incidence of signals passed at Danger, overspeeding and buffer stop collisions.

RI for their part have been independently considering what criteria they might apply to identifying parts of the network where measures to prevent these accidents are especially desirable and could be expected to yield value for money. We have asked HSE to report back in June 1995, on the progress that has been made in reaching agreement with Railtrack on such criteria, with an expectation of receiving a proposed strategy by that time.

Turning to the BR report, we are impressed by its openness and transparency, particularly the full statement of the data used; the clarity of the exposition, and the recognition of the important uncertainties. These have made it easier for us to assess the validity of the methodology used by BR and the robustness of the conclusions. We note that the report relates to a specific system of ATP, ie that piloted on the Chiltern and Great Western Lines. The conclusions reached in the report therefore apply only to that specific system and its associated costs. They do not necessarily apply to the generic concept of automatic train protection by technological means to complement the vigilance of the driver. Our views that follow must be seen in that light.

HSE experts have examined the report and believe that BR's approach is basically sound. However, they have questioned some of the assumptions made and would have carried out some of the cost calculations in a different way. Experts from HSE, British Rail (BR), and Railtrack have met to discuss and resolve technical issues. The main outcomes are set out in the Annex. As you will see, there are no substantial differences of view on the technical issues raised by the report. However, the issue of alternatives to the piloted ATP systems, to which we have referred above, remains unresolved.

HSE has made it clear in those discussions that any conclusions based on the assessment of the costs and benefits presented in the report are without prejudice to the Commission's view on the need to introduce some system or systems for preventing the kind of accidents that ATP are designed to avert. It is, in our view, a case of horses for courses and decisions should be made on a judgement of whether ATP as piloted or some variant, or alternative measures are, in given situations, reasonably practicable. Sir Bob Reid's letter of 31 March 1994 to John MacGregor made clear that if responsibility lay entirely with the British Railways Board, ATP or Automatic Train Control would be adopted as standard on new high speed lines including the Channel Tunnel rail link and will be given full consideration when Railtrack undertakes major resignalling works. The Commission regard this as the minimum response to the need and expect Railtrack to carry forward that undertaking by the British Railways Board.

The judgement on what is reasonably practicable can take as its starting point the philosophical framework (known as TOR) published by HSE[*] for deciding which risks are unacceptable, tolerable and broadly acceptable. This has gained considerable acceptance within industry (including the railway industry) and has helped to provide the basis for justifying decisions whereby risks are judged to be worth the benefits.

The framework involves acceptance of an upper limit above which a particular risk is regarded as unacceptable to HSE as a regulator. This upper limit is taken to be a chance of death of 1 in 1000 per annum for workers and 1 in 10 000 per annum for members of the public.

Below the upper limit is a region where a balance has to be struck between the costs and demonstrated benefits of any increments to the existing level of safety, ie of risk reduction. There must of course be confidence that a risk is actually being controlled at the relevant level, known as ALARP (as low as reasonably practicable). The lowest point at which it would be considered sensible to address any risk would be where the chance of death was about one in a million per year.

The BR target of 1 in 100 000 per year for the overall risk of death to regular commuters, one of the most exposed group of passengers, is already being achieved. The global application of ATP would therefore address degrees of risk which are in the lower portion of the 'ALARP' region. On the principles which HSE usually applies, this has two implications:

* *The tolerability of risk from nuclear power stations* HSE Books 1992 ISBN 0 11 886368 1

(a)   the value of life which has to be assumed in any balancing of cost and risk would not be enhanced by the factor of 'gross disproportion' which is applied to risks further up the tolerability scale, or where the chance is particularly hard to estimate.

(b)   it becomes reasonable to take into account the availability and value for money of alternative ways of making risk reducing investments.

An overall judgement as to the cost effectiveness of comprehensive application of any particular safety improvement will often mask situations where investment at particular locations may be cost effective while full application is not. In the case of ATP cost effectiveness at a particular location will depend on such factors as the frequency of services, the complexity of the system, and differing costs for more limited application.

Taking all these factors into account, HSE have told us that the introduction of ATP as piloted on a network-wide basis could not be regarded as reasonably practicable by the criteria they usually apply, and that there are alternative safety investments which would be likely to yield greater effectiveness in terms of lives saved, and better value for money. We endorse these judgements. However it would in our view be unreasonable to rule out the possibility that particular applications of ATP or indeed other automatic devices or other measures giving protection against ATP preventable accidents (ATPPAs) on parts of the network might yield good value in terms of reduced loss of life. We have taken into account, moreover, that there is a public expectation that automatic means of protection will be introduced at least on a partial basis, following on the information given by British Rail to the Hidden Inquiry and the latter's recommendations five years ago and in view of developments on some foreign railways. The European Commission's intention to introduce a directive on the inoperability of the high speed network in Europe, and the indications that the need to reduce accidents from signals passed at Danger will figure in their calculations is also a relevant factor.

The report refers to the prospects offered by alternative more advanced technology. The time-scale for its possible introduction is very uncertain and could be long especially bearing in mind the need to test and demonstrate any new system. At the same time, the emergence of modified and possibly cheaper versions of ATP than those so far tested by British Rail could lead to favourable outcomes in value for money terms, and should be pursued on an urgent basis.

Although Mr MacGregor invited us to do so, we would prefer not to pronounce on the vexed question of the value of life to be applied in such calculations. HSE have suggested that where catastrophic risk is concerned, the value cannot reasonably be less than three times the estimate which we understand your Department applies to situations of risk to individuals, and this conclusion was endorsed by Sir John Cullen in a letter to Mr MacGregor dated 9 November 1992. The BR report mentions for such applications a value of £3.5 million as a possibility. What does seem clear is that in any catastrophic accident, the damage in terms of public confidence, additional costs, and harms and risks to people quite aside from the number of deaths is substantially greater than damage connected with the generality of risks to individuals. While there may be two views about the rightness of factoring added costs to reflect this extra damage into the 'value for life', and we would prefer not to enter into this essentially technical argument, it seems obvious that they need to be taken into account in some way; and it is clear to us also that whatever balance is struck, it needs to be firmly on the side of safety where doubt arises.

In this respect, chapters 8 and 9 of the report seem relevant. These place the risks of ATP preventable accidents in context with other risks and examine the effects that investing in ATP would have on overall safety on the railways if its introduction were to displace other safety investments. In the time available, it has not been possible for HSE to evaluate the conclusions reached in these chapters. The Executive has, however, asked HMRI to take these factors into account, as well as the balance of costs and risks - in relation particularly to new investments - when they explore with Railtrack the possible options available for tackling ATP preventable accidents and possible criteria for identifying parts of the network where measures to prevent such accidents could yield value for money.

As I said at the outset, we have asked for a report on the outcome of these discussions by June 1995. The report from BR has acted most usefully as a catalyst. We now need to move towards achieving a solution to what we regard as an issue of serious concern.

$$\boxed{\textbf{APPENDIX 12b}}$$

OUTCOME OF DISCUSSIONS ON TECHNICAL ISSUES BETWEEN HSE AND RAILTRACK EXPERTS ON BR ATP REPORT

(a) **A revision of the yearly average number of equivalent fatalities.** The report had estimated that ATP preventable accidents (ATPPAs) would give rise on average to 4.3 equivalent fatalities by looking at the historical record of ATPPAs over the past 26 years. Providentially, however, this record does not include any catastrophic ATPPAs and it was agreed that a forecast of ATP effectiveness needs to allow for such events. The way this might be done is a matter for technical debate. HSE believe that the resulting average number of lives hypothetically saved would lie between 5.5 and 6.5. Railtrack calculate an average between 4.3 and 5.5, preferably towards the lower end of this range, but in the spirit of compromise was prepared to accept a best estimate of 5.5.

(b) **A revision of the cost of ATP per fatality avoided.** The effect of using the revised figures above were that:

 (i) fitment of the ATP system, on the whole network as described in the BR report, would cost between £9.2 m and £14 m per fatality avoided with the best estimate of £10.9 m; and

 (ii) selective fitment would cost between £4.5 m - £7 m per fatality avoided with the best estimate of £5.5 m.

(c) **Agreement that there might exist cheaper automatic systems alternative to ATP as piloted, which might be unsuitable for whole network applications but which might offer better value for heightened protection in particular situations.** Railtrack while outlining certain possibilities of this kind for alternative technologies or for systems using some but not all the features of ATP as piloted have so far been unable to give us indications which are sufficiently specific as to method, cost or timing for us to take into account in this letter. HSE have encouraged them to pursue these possibilities as quickly as possible.

(d) **Agreement that there were differences between HSE, Railtrack and BR on the methodology that should be adopted for conducting cost benefit analysis.** Though these raised points of principle, ie the rates that should be used for discounting future costs and benefits, they did not materially affect the conclusions reached about the cost of ATP as piloted.

APPENDIX 12c

REPLY FROM THE SECRETARY OF STATE IN THE HOUSE OF COMMONS

Mr Bob Dunn (Con - Dartford):
To ask the Secretary of State for Transport, what advice he has received from the Health and Safety Commission (HSC) and Railtrack on British Rail's report on Automatic Train Protection (ATP), and if he will make a statement.

DR BRIAN MAWHINNEY

Serious railway accidents are relatively rare and there has been a significant improvement in railway safety in recent years. Accidents involving signals passed at danger, overspeeding and buffer stop collisions, which ATP would prevent, are infrequent and account for about 3% of fatalities and injuries (excluding trespassers and suicides). The trend in the number of serious incidents where signals have been passed at danger (SPAD) has been downward in the last five years. But there is no room for complacency about the need to pursue cost effective measures to reduce the risk of accidents to the lowest reasonably practicable level.

The British Rail (BR) report on ATP examined the technical feasibility, costs and benefits of two pilot ATP systems. Copies of the report were placed in the Library of the House last July. The HSC and Railtrack have concluded that the report was thorough and sound. I welcome that conclusion.

On the basis of advice I have received from the HSC, I have concluded that applications of ATP, other automatic devices or measures giving protection against ATP-preventable accidents may be justified on parts of the network. In particular, the HSC has asked the Health and Safety Executive to explore with Railtrack the options for tackling ATP-preventable accidents, and the criteria that might be used for identifying parts of the network where such measures could yield value for money, with a view to receiving a proposed strategy from Railtrack by June 1995. In addition and in the longer term, the HSC has advised me that ATP or Automatic Train Control (ATC) should be adopted as standard on new high speed lines including the Channel Tunnel Rail Link, and that full consideration should be given to installing ATP functions within future major resignalling works, such as modernisation of the West Coast Main Line.

BR and Railtrack have advised me that network-wide fitment of ATP as piloted is not justifiable because the costs far outweigh the benefits. The HSC has endorsed this view and, furthermore, considers that there are alternative safety investments which would be likely to yield greater effectiveness in terms of lives saved, and better value for money. The BR report on ATP has demonstrated the importance of assessing the costs and benefits of all investment aimed at improving safety to ensure that funding goes to schemes which maximise the benefits for rail users. Copies of the HSC's full advice, which I accept in full, have been placed in the Library of the House.

British Rail and Railtrack remain committed to a co-ordinated programme to reduce the risks associated with signals passed at danger, overspeeding and buffer stop collisions. As part of this programme, the feasibility of a drivers' reminder device is being researched which will help prevent drivers stopped at danger signals from inadvertently starting against these signals when the train is ready to move, for example at a station. This is one of the more common types of SPAD leading to serious consequences and such a device could potentially deliver up to 25% of the benefits of network-wide ATP. An early trial of this device is proposed.

A further project is examining enhancement of the present Automatic Warning System (AWS) so that the brakes are applied automatically if a train approaches a red signal at excessive speed indicating an impending signal passed at danger or over-speeding incident. A detailed specification is being drawn up.

Risk analysis is also being applied to track layout and signalling design, to ensure that safety factors are taken into account quantitatively in the design of the network. Protective signalling measures have already been introduced at a number of vulnerable locations and examination of other vulnerable locations is ongoing.

Railtrack is giving high priority to the development of appropriate techniques for quantifying the costs and benefits of these projects and considering their application at individual locations.

ATP and other devices are not the only way of preventing or mitigating certain risks. The human factors involved will continue to be addressed through driver selection, training, motivation and supervision programmes. This includes close attention to driver familiarisation when new rolling stock and signalling is introduced, and a rigorous alcohol and drugs policy.

The Chiltern Line and Great Western pilot ATP installations will continue in service, and ATP will be extended to the new Heathrow Express Link in due course. The scope for improvement in the cost/benefit ratio of ATP will continue to be examined through these schemes.

I have asked the HSC for an overall progress report in July.

Printed and published in the UK by the Health and Safety Executive   11/95   C20

This Statutory Instrument has been made in consequence of a defect in S.I. 1998/1340 and is being issued free of charge to all known recipients of that Statutory Instrument

STATUTORY INSTRUMENTS

1998 No. 1519

TRANSPORT

The Railways (Amendment) Regulations 1998

ISBN 0-11-079364-1

9 780110 793641 >

(b) the rail transport activities in Great Britain of and the charging of infrastructure fees to railway undertakings established or to be established in an EEA State and international groupings which they form; and

(c) the licensing of such undertakings and groupings in respect of international services and international combined transport goods services which they operate.

(2) These Regulations do not apply to–

(a) railway undertakings whose activities are limited to the operation of urban, suburban or regional services; and

(b) the management of the tunnel system and the rail transport activity of the Concessionaires in respect of any shuttle service.

PART II
INFRASTRUCTURE MANAGEMENT

Separation of accounts between transport operations and infrastructure management and prohibition of transfer of state aid

5. Any railway undertaking which is also an infrastructure manager shall–

(a) prepare and maintain accounts for business relating to the provision of transport services, which are separate from its accounts for business relating to the management of railway infrastructure; and

(b) ensure that there is no transfer of state aid granted to the undertaking between the provision of transport services and the management of railway infrastructure.

Balancing infrastructure fees and infrastructure expenditure

6.—(1) An infrastructure manager shall ensure that, under normal business conditions over a reasonable period of time, the expenditure on railway infrastructure which he incurs does not exceed the income which he receives from infrastructure fees and State contributions.

(2) An infrastructure manager may finance the development of railway infrastructure, including the provision or renewal of capital assets, and may make a return on the capital employed in his undertaking.

Calculation of, and rules for the determination of, fees for the use of railway infrastructure

7.—(1) Infrastructure managers shall charge, and be paid, fees for the use by railway undertakings and international groupings of railway infrastructure for which they are responsible.

(2) Infrastructure fees shall be determined so as to avoid any discrimination in the charging for services of an equivalent nature in the same market.

(3) Infrastructure fees shall be determined in accordance with the rules in Schedule 1 and, in relation to a fee to be charged under an agreement which is an access contract entered into pursuant to a direction under section 17 or 18 of the Railways Act 1993, it shall fall to the Regulator, in consultation with the infrastructure manager and the person by whom the fee is payable or a person acting on his behalf, to determine the fee in accordance with those rules as if in rules 2, 4 and 5 the references to an amount determined by agreement were references to an amount determined by the Regulator in consultation with those persons.

(4) The rules in Schedule 1 apply to the determination of fees on the conclusion, modification or renewal of agreements for the use of railway infrastructure.

Information to be provided by infrastructure managers

8.—(1) Whenever requested in writing to do so by the International Rail Regulator, an infrastructure manager shall provide him with such information concerning infrastructure fees charged by that infrastructure manager as the International Rail Regulator shall consider necessary to enable him to decide whether or not infrastructure fees are charged on a non-discriminatory basis.

(2) An infrastructure manager shall inform in good time railway undertakings using the railway infrastructure operated by that infrastructure manager in order · to provide international services and international combined transport goods services of any major changes in the quality or capacity of the railway infrastructure concerned.

International Rail Regulator

9.—(1) There shall continue to be an officer known as the "International Rail Regulator" appointed by the Secretary of State to perform the functions conferred on him by these Regulations.

(2) The Secretary of State shall appoint a person to hold office as the International Rail Regulator.

(3) An appointment of a person to hold the office as the International Rail Regulator shall be for a term not exceeding five years, but previous appointment to that office shall not affect eligibility for re-appointment.

(4) The Secretary of State may remove a person from office as the International Rail Regulator on the ground of incapacity or misbehaviour.

(5) Subject to paragraphs (3) and (4), a person appointed as the International Rail Regulator shall hold and vacate office as such in accordance with the terms of his appointment.

(6) The provisions of Schedule 2 shall have effect with respect to the International Rail Regulator.

(7) At any time when there is no person holding office as the International Rail Regulator the functions conferred on the holder of that office by these Regulations shall be exercisable by the Secretary of State.

PART III
ACCESS AND TRANSIT MATTERS

Allocation bodies

10.—(1) The Secretary of State shall, after consulting the International Rail Regulator and such allocation bodies and infrastructure managers as appear to him to be appropriate, designate one or more infrastructure managers to be allocation bodies and specify the classes or descriptions of applications for access or transit rights in respect of which each such manager is to act as the allocation body.

(2) As soon as practicable after designating an allocation body pursuant to paragraph (1) the Secretary of State shall procure publication of a notice in the Official Journal of the European Communities containing the following particulars–

    (a) the name of the allocation body and the address to which applications for the allocation of infrastructure capacity should be sent; and

    (b) the classes or descriptions of applications for access or transit rights in respect of which the allocation body is to act as such.

(3) Any allocation body and any infrastructure manager shall ensure that such capacity is allocated on a fair and non-discriminatory basis.

(4) The Secretary of State may give directions to any allocation body or infrastructure manager for the purpose of ensuring that priority in the allocation of infrastructure capacity is given to rail services provided–

(a) pursuant to Council Regulation (EEC) No 1191/69 on public service obligations in transport(**a**); or

(b) wholly or partly operated on infrastructure constructed or developed for specialised high speed or freight services.

(5) Where the Secretary of State has given a direction pursuant to paragraph (4)(a) which imposes a particular allocation of infrastructure capacity in the interests of public service, and which results in an infrastructure manager sustaining financial loss, he shall pay to that manager such compensation in respect of the loss as the Secretary of State thinks fair and reasonable in the circumstances of the case.

(6) The Secretary of State may give directions to any allocation body or infrastructure manager requiring the grant of access or transit rights to railway undertakings providing particular types of services or providing services in particular areas if in his opinion the grant of such rights is indispensable to secure the provision of adequate public services, the efficient use of railway infrastructure or the financing of new railway infrastructure.

(7) It shall be the duty of any person to whom the Secretary of State gives a direction pursuant to this regulation to comply with and give effect to the direction.

(8) Each allocation body and infrastructure manager shall in allocating infrastructure capacity have regard to any guidance issued by the International Rail Regulator after consultation with the Secretary of State.

Allocation of infrastructure capacity: application in Great Britain

11.—(1) Any international grouping may make an application–

(a) in the case of a grouping which includes a railway undertaking established in the United Kingdom, for such access and transit rights, or

(b) in the case of any other grouping, for such transit rights,

as may be necessary for the provision of international transport services between the EEA States where the undertakings constituting the grouping are established.

(2) Any railway undertaking established or to be established in an EEA State may make an application for the grant of such access and transit rights as may be necessary for the purpose of the operation of international combined transport goods services.

(3) Any agreement for the grant of access or transit rights to which paragraph (1) or (2) applies which is entered into otherwise than in pursuance of this Part shall be void.

(4) Any application referred to in paragraph (1) or (2) shall be in writing and shall be made to the allocation body designated pursuant to paragraph (1) of regulation 10 in respect of the class or description of application within which the application falls ("the GB allocation body") whenever the departure point of the service in question is situated in Great Britain.

(5) On receipt by the GB allocation body of any such application, that body shall immediately send a copy of the application to any relevant infrastructure manager and to any relevant EEA allocation body.

(6) As soon as possible, but in any event no later than one month, after receiving all relevant information relating to such an application any relevant EEA allocation body and any relevant infrastructure manager shall decide whether to grant or to refuse the application and shall immediately inform the GB allocation body of its decision.

(7) As soon as possible, but in any event no later than two months, after receiving all relevant information relating to such an application the GB allocation body shall, together with each relevant EEA allocation body and each relevant infrastructure manager, decide whether the application should be granted or refused and shall inform the applicant of the decision.

(8) If an application is refused, the GB allocation body shall give to the applicant the reasons for such refusal.

(9) Where an application has been refused on the grounds of insufficient capacity, the GB allocation body, any relevant EEA allocation body and any relevant infrastructure

---

(**a**) OJ No. L156, 28.6.69, p.1. Amended by Regulation (EEC) No. 1893/91 (OJ No. L169, 29.6.91, p.1).

manager shall if the applicant so requests reconsider the application on the next occasion that the timetables for the routes concerned are adjusted.

(10) The GB allocation body shall on request furnish interested parties with details of the dates of all relevant timetable adjustments and other administrative arrangements as they may reasonably require in connection with any request or proposed request under paragraph (9).

(11) The GB allocation body, any relevant EEA allocation body and any relevant infrastructure manager may require the payment of a charge to cover their reasonable costs of dealing with an application.

(12) Every international grouping and every railway undertaking to which railway infrastructure capacity is allocated in accordance with these Regulations shall conclude an agreement with each relevant infrastructure manager covering the necessary administrative, technical and financial matters to regulate traffic control and safety issues concerning the services to be provided by them.

(13) An agreement concluded pursuant to paragraph (12) shall include provision requiring the parties thereto to make such amendments thereto as the International Rail Regulator may direct in order to give effect to any decision he makes on a reference to him under regulation 14.

(14) The terms and conditions of an agreement concluded pursuant to paragraph (12) shall not be discriminatory between railway undertakings or between railway undertakings and the infrastructure manager as a provider of rail services.

(15) Within fourteen days of the conclusion of an agreement pursuant to paragraph (12) each relevant infrastructure manager shall send a copy thereof to the Regulator and the International Rail Regulator and shall notify the GB allocation body and each relevant EEA allocation body of the conclusion of the agreement.

(16) Within twenty one days of receiving a copy of such an agreement the International Rail Regulator shall procure publication of a notice in the Official Journal of the European Communities including the following particulars–
  (a) the name of the applicant railway undertaking or international grouping;
  (b) the name of the GB allocation body, each relevant infrastructure manager and relevant EEA allocation body;
  (c) brief particulars of the access or transit rights granted; and
  (d) a statement that any railway undertaking aggrieved by the decision of the GB allocation body as given effect by the agreement may by notice in writing refer the matter to the International Rail Regulator.

(17) The International Rail Regulator shall if so requested in writing by a railway undertaking which he reasonably considers has an interest in the matter provide to that undertaking such particulars of the agreement as that undertaking may reasonably require, including particulars as to the infrastructure fees payable under the agreement.

(18) In making information available pursuant to paragraph (17) the International Rail Regulator shall have regard to the need for excluding, so far as practicable, any particulars of or about the agreement which, if disclosed, would or might in the opinion of the International Rail Regulator seriously and prejudicially affect the interests of any party to the agreement.

(19) Any infrastructure manager which grants access or transit rights under this regulation shall so operate its control and safety systems as to take account of the services operated in exercise of such rights.

(20) Nothing in this regulation shall be taken to prevent an applicant from making direct contact with any relevant EEA allocation body but, if it does so, it shall so inform the GB allocation body.

(21) In this regulation and regulations 12, 13 and 14–
  "EEA allocation body" means an allocation body in an EEA State other than the United Kingdom;
  "GB allocation body" has the meaning given by paragraph (4);

"relevant EEA allocation body" means an EEA allocation body which is responsible for the allocation of capacity on railway infrastructure to which the application relates; and

"relevant infrastructure manager" means any infrastructure manager which manages infrastructure in Great Britain to which the application relates (including any allocation body which is also such an infrastructure manager).

Allocation of infrastructure capacity: application outside Great Britain

12.—(1) On receipt by a GB allocation body from an EEA allocation body of a copy of an application for access or transit rights made to the EEA allocation body, the GB allocation body shall immediately send a copy of the application to any relevant infrastructure manager.

(2) As soon as possible but in any event no later than three weeks after receiving all relevant information relating to the application, any such infrastructure manager shall decide whether to grant or to refuse the application in respect of the infrastructure which it manages and shall immediately after making the decision inform the GB allocation body thereof.

(3) As soon as possible but in any event no later than one week after being informed of the decision of each relevant infrastructure manager, the GB allocation body shall inform the EEA allocation body of each such decision.

(4) If an application for infrastructure capacity is refused, the GB allocation body shall give to the EEA allocation body the reasons for such refusal, and if such an application is granted the GB allocation body shall promptly notify the International Rail Regulator of that decision and provide him with the following particulars–
  (a) the name of the applicant, railway undertaking or international grouping;
  (b) the name of the GB allocation body, each relevant infrastructure manager and relevant EEA allocation body; and
  (c) brief particulars of the access or transit rights granted.

(5) Paragraphs (9) to (19) and (21) of regulation 11 shall have effect in relation to applications to which this regulation applies with the following modifications–
  (a) subject to sub-paragraph (c) references to any relevant EEA allocation body shall be disregarded;
  (b) in paragraph (9) the reference to the applicant shall be read as a reference to the EEA allocation body acting at the request of the applicant; and
  (c) in paragraph (15) the reference to each relevant EEA allocation body shall be read as a reference to the EEA allocation body.

Safety certificates

13.—(1) No railway undertaking or international grouping may exercise access or transit rights contained in an agreement with an infrastructure manager concluded pursuant to regulation 11 or 12 unless the undertaking or grouping has produced to the infrastructure manager a safety certificate.

(2) For the purposes of paragraph (1) a safety certificate is any document issued by the Health and Safety Executive confirming that–
  (a) (i) the railway undertaking or international grouping has prepared a safety case under regulation 4 of the Railways (Safety Case) Regulations 1994(**a**) in respect of the operation of trains under the agreement;
      (ii) the safety case has been accepted by the relevant infrastructure controller (as defined in the said regulation 4); and
      (iii) the Health and Safety Executive is satisfied with the safety case; or
  (b) the railway undertaking or international grouping is exempt from the said regulation 4 when it operates trains under the agreement.

(**a**) S.I. 1994/237.

8

Appeals in respect of allocation of infrastructure capacity or the charging of fees

14.—(1) A railway undertaking aggrieved by a decision of the GB allocation body under regulation 11 or 12 for the allocation of railway infrastructure capacity or the charging of infrastructure fees may refer the matter to the International Rail Regulator.

(2) In the case of a decision to refuse an application, such notice shall be given by the applicant within twenty one days of being informed of the decision.

(3) In the case of a decision to grant an application, such notice shall be given within two months of the publication of the particulars of any agreement made pursuant to the decision in the Official Journal of the European Communities in accordance with paragraph (16) of regulation 11 (including that paragraph as applied by paragraph (5) of regulation 12).

(4) Any railway undertaking which refers a decision to the International Rail Regulator under paragraph (1) shall at the same time provide a statement of the reasons why it is aggrieved by the decision.

(5) The International Rail Regulator shall, within seven days of receiving such a notice and a statement of reasons, send a copy thereof to the Regulator, the GB allocation body, any relevant EEA allocation body, the relevant infrastructure manager and the international grouping or railway undertaking concerned.

(6) Any person notified under paragraph (5) may, within twenty one days of receiving such a copy, make such representations as he considers appropriate to the International Rail Regulator concerning the decision to which the notice relates and the statement of reasons.

(7) The International Rail Regulator shall reach a determination on a reference made under this regulation within two months of the date of receiving all relevant information (including any information provided pursuant to paragraph (12)) to enable him to determine the reference.

(8) On disposing of a reference under this regulation the International Rail Regulator may decide that the GB allocation body's decision should stand, be reversed or be modified.

(9) Where the decision of the International Rail Regulator requires the modification of any agreement made pursuant to an allocation body's decision or the grant of rights where an application has been refused he may give such directions as he thinks fit for that purpose and the infrastructure manager and railway undertaking concerned shall be under a duty to comply with and give effect to any such directions.

(10) The International Rail Regulator shall not make a decision requiring the grant of rights by an infrastructure manager or the modification of rights granted by an infrastructure manager unless he is satisfied that the grant would not involve the breach by the infrastructure manager of the duty imposed on him by paragraph (3) of regulation 10 or of any direction given by the Secretary of State pursuant to paragraph (4) of that regulation.

(11) If on a reference to the International Rail Regulator under the preceding provisions of this regulation a question arises as to any matter which may, in the opinion of the International Rail Regulator, have safety implications, he shall refer the question to the Health and Safety Executive whose opinion on the question shall be taken into account by the International Rail Regulator.

(12) It shall be the duty of any railway undertaking, any infrastructure manager and any GB allocation body to provide the International Rail Regulator with such information as he may reasonably require for the purpose of determining a reference to him under this regulation.

PART IV

INTERNATIONAL LICENCES

Prohibition of unlicensed provision of international services

15.—(1) Subject to paragraph (4) no person may provide international services in Great Britain or international combined transport goods services in Great Britain unless he is

authorised to do so by an international licence, and any person who provides such services without such a licence shall be guilty of an offence.

(2) Any person who is guilty of an offence under this regulation shall be liable–

(a) on summary conviction, to a fine not exceeding the statutory maximum;

(b) on conviction on indictment, to a fine.

(3) No proceedings shall be instituted in England and Wales in respect of an offence under this regulation except by or on behalf of the Secretary of State or the International Rail Regulator.

(4) This regulation does not apply to the provision of services to which paragraph (1) applies prior to 28th September 1998 if and to the extent that the operation of railway assets for the purposes of such provision is authorised by a licence granted under Part I of the Railways Act 1993 which was granted before 27th June 1998, but any such licence shall to that extent be revoked on 28th September 1998.

(5) In this regulation the expression "international licence" includes a licence granted pursuant to any action taken by an EEA State for the purpose of implementing Council Directive No. 95/18/EC.

Appointment of licensing authority and grant of international licences

16.—(1) The International Rail Regulator is hereby designated as the person responsible for granting international licences.

(2) Subject to and in accordance with these Regulations, the International Rail Regulator shall, on an application in writing made to him by a railway undertaking established in Great Britain in such form and manner as he may from time to time prescribe, grant to that railway undertaking an international licence.

(3) An international licence may authorise the provision of services generally or be restricted to particular types of service specified in the licence.

(4) Before granting or modifying an international licence the International Rail Regulator shall consult the Health and Safety Executive.

(5) An applicant shall submit with his application such application fee as the International Rail Regulator may reasonably require and the information about the applicant referred to in Schedule 3 and at any time after submitting the application such further information as the International Rail Regulator may reasonably require in connection with the application.

(6) The applicant shall at the same time as he submits any information about his professional competence to the International Rail Regulator send to the Health and Safety Executive a copy of that information.

(7) The International Rail Regulator shall grant an international licence if, and only if, he is satisfied that the applicant will be able at any time to satisfy the requirements referred to in Schedule 3 as to good repute, financial fitness, professional competence and cover for liabilities to third parties.

(8) An application for an international licence shall be determined by the International Rail Regulator as soon as possible and in any event within three months of receipt of the information referred to in paragraph (5).

(9) In respect of each application for an international licence the International Rail Regulator shall publish at least once in the Official Journal of the European Communities, the London Gazette, the Edinburgh Gazette and in one or more newspapers whose circulation together covers the whole of Great Britain a notice including the following particulars:–

(a) a statement that the applicant has made an application for an international licence and the principal address of the International Rail Regulator;

(b) the name of the applicant and the address of its registered or principal office; and

10

    (c) a summary of the activities which the applicant wishes to carry out pursuant to the international licence.

    (10) The International Rail Regulator shall inform the applicant in writing of his decision and, where he refuses to grant an international licence, the refusal shall state the reasons for his decision.

    (11) As soon as practicable after granting an international licence the International Rail Regulator shall send a copy of the licence to the Regulator and to the Health and Safety Executive.

    (12) Any sums received by the International Rail Regulator under this regulation shall be paid into the Consolidated Fund.

    (13) Schedule 3 shall have effect.

Modification of international licences

    17.—(1) The International Rail Regulator may modify an international licence if the holder of the licence consents to the modification.

    (2) Before modifying an international licence the International Rail Regulator shall consult the Health and Safety Executive.

    (3) As soon as practicable after modifying an international licence the International Rail Regulator shall send a copy to the Regulator and to the Health and Safety Executive.

Validity of international licences

    18. An international licence shall, unless previously revoked or surrendered in accordance with any provision in these Regulations or the licence, continue in force for as long as the railway undertaking concerned complies with the requirements of these Regulations and any conditions included in the licence.

Monitoring, suspension and revocation of international licences

    19.—(1) If at any time the International Rail Regulator considers that there is serious doubt whether a railway undertaking to which an international licence has been granted complies with a requirement of these Regulations or a condition included in the licence, he may take such steps as are necessary to enable him to determine whether or not the undertaking does so comply.

    (2) Where the serious doubt of the International Rail Regulator relates wholly or partly to the requirement of professional competence such steps shall include consulting the Health and Safety Executive.

    (3) If, having taken the steps referred to in paragraph (1), the International Rail Regulator is satisfied that a railway undertaking to which an international licence has been granted does not comply with any such requirement, he shall revoke the licence or suspend it for such period as he thinks fit.

    (4) The International Rail Regulator shall revoke an international licence if proceedings have been commenced for the winding up of a railway undertaking to which an international licence has been granted on the grounds that the undertaking is unable to pay its debts and he is satisfied that there is no reasonable prospect of satisfactory financial restructuring of the undertaking within a reasonable period of time.

    (5) Where the International Rail Regulator is satisfied that there is serious doubt whether a railway undertaking to which an international licence has been granted by a licensing authority other than himself complies with any requirement of Council Directive No. 95/18/EC he shall without delay so notify that licensing authority.

    (6) Where the International Rail Regulator has suspended or revoked an international licence solely on the grounds of the non-compliance by the railway undertaking with the requirements of financial fitness specified in Schedule 3, but he considers that there is a realistic prospect of a satisfactory financial restructuring of the undertaking taking place within a reasonable period of time, he may grant to the undertaking a temporary international licence pending such financial restructuring.

(7) A temporary international licence granted under paragraph (6) shall not be granted where the International Rail Regulator after consultation with the Health and Safety Executive considers that safety would be jeopardised.

(8) A temporary international licence granted under paragraph (6) shall not be granted for a period exceeding six months.

(9) Where a railway undertaking to which an international licence has been granted has either ceased the operations to which the licence relates or has not commenced such operations within six months of the date of such grant then the International Rail Regulator may either require the railway undertaking to resubmit its licence to him for approval or suspend the licence.

(10) Where the International Rail Regulator has required a railway undertaking to resubmit its international licence in pursuance of paragraph (9) on the grounds that the railway undertaking has not commenced such operations the railway undertaking shall be entitled to request that a period longer than the six months be granted in which it can commence operations. In considering such a request the International Rail Regulator shall take account of the specific nature of the services to be provided by the railway undertaking under the international licence.

(11) In the event of a change to a railway undertaking's legal situation, in particular following a change in the control or ownership of the railway undertaking as a result of a merger with or take-over by another undertaking, the International Rail Regulator may require the railway undertaking to resubmit its licence to him for review. The railway undertaking may continue operations while its licence is under review unless the International Rail Regulator is satisfied after consultation with the Health and Safety Executive that safety is jeopardised by the change and so notifies the undertaking.

(12) When a railway undertaking intends significantly to change or extend its activities from those in respect of which a licence was granted to it, the railway undertaking shall resubmit its licence to the International Rail Regulator for review.

(13) When the International Rail Regulator suspends, revokes or amends an international licence in accordance with this regulation he shall forthwith inform the Commission of such amendment, revocation or suspension.

Conditions of international licences

20.—(1) An international licence shall include conditions requiring the licence holder to satisfy requirements as to the good repute, financial fitness, professional competence and cover for liabilities to third parties of the licence holder, including those requirements specified in Schedule 3, and may include conditions–

    (a) requiring the licence holder to submit to a review of its licence at least every five years during the currency of the licence;

    (b) concerning the suspension or revocation of the licence.

(2) Without prejudice to the generality of paragraph (1) licence conditions may require the licence holder to make a payment to the International Rail Regulator on the grant of the licence and to make such further payments during the currency of the licence, the amount or amounts to be determined by the International Rail Regulator.

(3) Any sums received by the International Rail Regulator under paragraph (2) shall be paid into the Consolidated Fund.

PART V

MISCELLANEOUS

Amendment of Railways Act 1993

21.—(1) The Railways Act 1993 shall be amended in accordance with the following provisions of this regulation.

(2) After subsection (1) insert–

    "(1A) This section does not apply to a person who acts as the operator of a railway

asset to the extent that the asset is operated for the purpose of providing international services".

(3) In subsection (2) of that section, before the definition of "operator", insert the following definitions–

"'international licence' means a licence granted pursuant to a provision contained in subordinate legislation made for the purpose of implementing the Directive of the Council of the European Union dated 19th June 1995 on the licensing of railway undertakings or pursuant to any action taken by an EEA State for that purpose;" and

"'international services' means services the provision of which requires an international licence;".

(4) After subsection (2) of section 6 there shall be inserted the following subsection–

"(2A) In subsection (2) above "EEA State" means a State which is a Contracting Party to the Agreement on the European Economic Area signed at Oporto on 2nd May 1992 as adjusted by the Protocol signed at Brussels on 17th March 1993;".

(5) In subsection (1) of section 17 delete the word "or" after paragraph (b) and after paragraph (c) insert "or" followed by–

"(d) the permission to use a railway facility to which the application relates could be applied for under subordinate legislation made for the purpose of implementing Council Directive 95/19/EC on the allocation of railway infrastructure capacity and the charging of infrastructure fees.".

(6) In subsection (7) of section 17 for the definition of "the Directive" substitute the following definition–

"'the Directives' mean Council Directive No. 91/440/EEC on the development of the Community's railways and Council Directive No. 95/19/EC on the allocation of railway infrastructure capacity and the charging of infrastructure fees;".

(7) In that subsection, in the definition of "implementing regulation" substitute "the Directives" for "the Directive" in both places.

(8) In that subsection, in the definition of "international railway access contract"–

(a) substitute "the Directives" for "the Directive" in both places;

(b) substitute "allocation body" for "infrastructure manager" in both places; and

(c) delete "other than the United Kingdom".

(9) In subsection (1) of section 83, after the definition of "installation owner", insert–

"'international licence' has the meaning given by section 6(2) above;".

(10) In subsection (2) of section 145, at the end of paragraph (g) insert–

"or Council Directive 95/18/EC on the licensing of railway undertakings or Council Directive 95/19/EC on the allocation of railway infrastructure capacity and the charging of infrastructure fees".

Statutory authority to run trains

22. Any international grouping or railway undertaking granted access or transit rights under these Regulations shall, if and to the extent that it would not, apart from this regulation, have statutory authority to run trains over any track in exercise of such rights, be taken to have statutory authority to do so.

International groupings and railway undertakings granted access or transit rights not to be common carriers

23. International groupings and railway undertakings granted access or transit rights under these Regulations shall not in relation to the provision of international services in exercise of those rights be regarded as common carriers by railway.

Application of enactments concerning railways

24. Paragraphs 2 (disapplication of enactments in the case of Concessionaires and through service operators), 3 (extension of enactments in relation to through service operators) and 4 (modification of enactments applying to Concessionaires and through

service operators) of Schedule 6 to the Channel Tunnel Act 1987 shall apply to international groupings and railway undertakings, other than the Concessionaires and the British Railways Board, in relation to the provision of international services in exercise of access or transit rights under these Regulations who are not through service operators within the meaning of that Schedule as they apply to those who are.

International groupings

25. In the event of a contravention of, or a refusal or failure to comply with, a requirement or prohibition imposed by these Regulations on an international grouping–

(a) where the contravention, or refusal or failure to comply would be an offence under these Regulations or under the Health and Safety at Work, etc. Act 1974(**a**) each railway undertaking comprised in the grouping shall be guilty of the offence and liable to be proceeded against and punished accordingly; and

(b) where a civil remedy would be available to any person in respect of any loss, damage or injury caused by the contravention, or refusal or failure to comply, each railway undertaking comprised in the grouping shall be jointly and severally liable in respect of such loss, damage or injury.

Civil proceedings

26.—(1) The obligation to comply with regulation 5, paragraph (1) of regulation 6, paragraph (2) of regulation 7, paragraph (2) of regulation 8, paragraph (3) of regulation 10, or paragraphs (12) and (14) of regulation 11 (including those paragraphs as applied by paragraph (5) of regulation 12), a decision under paragraph (8) or direction under paragraph (9) of regulation 14, or the rules specified in Schedule 1 shall be a duty owed to any person who may be affected by a breach of that duty and shall be actionable by any such person who sustains loss, damage or injury caused by the breach at the suit or instance of that person.

(2) In any proceedings brought against an allocation body, infrastructure manager, international grouping or railway undertaking in pursuance of paragraph (1), it shall be defence for it to prove that it took all reasonable steps and exercised all due diligence to avoid the breach of duty.

(3) Without prejudice to the right which any person may have by virtue of paragraph (1) to bring civil proceedings in respect of any breach of duty, the obligation to comply shall be enforceable by civil proceedings by the International Rail Regulator for an injunction or for interdict or any other relief.

Making of false statements etc.

27.—(1) If any person, in giving any information or making any application under or for the purposes of any provision of these Regulations, makes any statement which he knows to be false in a material particular, he is guilty of an offence and shall be liable–

(a) on summary conviction, to a fine not exceeding the statutory maximum;

(b) on conviction on indictment, to a fine.

(2) No proceedings shall be instituted in England or Wales in respect of an offence under this regulation except by or with the consent of the Secretary of State or the Director of Public Prosecutions.

Offences by bodies corporate and Scottish partnerships

28.—(1) Where an offence under these Regulations has been committed by a body corporate and it is proved to have been committed with the consent or connivance of, or to be attributable to any neglect on the part of, any director, manager, secretary or other similar officer of the body corporate or any person who was purporting to act in any such capacity, he as well as the body corporate shall be guilty of that offence and be liable to be proceeded against and punished accordingly.

(**a**) 1974 c.37.

14

(2) Where the affairs of a body corporate are managed by its members, paragraph (1) shall apply in relation to the acts and defaults of a member in connection with his functions of management as if he were a director of the body corporate.

(3) Where a Scottish partnership is guilty of an offence under these Regulations in Scotland and that offence is proved to have been committed with the consent or connivance of, or to be attributable to any neglect on the part of, a partner, he as well as the partnership shall be guilty of that offence and shall be liable to be proceeded against and punished accordingly.

Restrictions on disclosure of information

29. Section 145 of the Railways Act 1993 shall have effect in relation to information which has been obtained under or by virtue of any provision of these Regulations and which relates to the affairs of any individual or to any particular business as it has effect in relation to such information obtained under or by virtue of any of the provisions of that Act.

Offences outside the United Kingdom

30.—(1) For the purpose of determining whether a breach of the duty imposed by regulation 5 has occurred, it is immaterial that the relevant acts or omissions occurred outside the United Kingdom if, when they occurred, the person—

(a) was a United Kingdom national, or

(b) was a body incorporated under the law of any part of the United Kingdom, or

(c) was a person (other than a United Kingdom national or such a body) maintaining a place of business in the United Kingdom.

(2) In this regulation "United Kingdom national" means an individual who is—

(a) a British citizen, a British Dependent Territories citizen, a British National (Overseas) or a British Overseas citizen;

(b) a person who under the British Nationality Act 1981(**a**) is a British subject, or

(c) a British protected person (within the meaning of that Act).

Signed by authority of the Secretary of State for the Environment, Transport and the Regions

Glenda Jackson
Parliamentary Under Secretary of State,
Department of the Environment,
Transport and the Regions

30th May 1998

SCHEDULE 1   Regulation 7(4)

ACCESS FEES

1.   Subject to rules 2 to 5, a fee for the use of infrastructure shall include, and shall include only:–

(a) an amount equal to the estimated costs reasonably attributable to the operation of trains in pursuance of the agreement under which the fee is payable; and

(b) an amount determined in accordance with rule 2 in respect of a share of estimated common costs.

2.   The amount referred to in rule 1(b) shall be such amount as may be determined by agreement between the infrastructure manager and the person by whom the fee is payable or a person acting on his behalf.

3.   In determining a fee, account shall be taken of the nature of the service, the time of the service, the market situation and the type and degree of wear and tear of the infrastructure.

(**a**) 1981 c.61.

4. A fee may be increased or decreased by an amount determined by agreement between the infrastructure manager and the person by whom the fee is payable or a person acting on his behalf to take account of special or exclusive rights to use the infrastructure granted to the person by whom the fee is payable or to any other person.

5. A fee may be increased or decreased, in accordance with any performance incentive regime agreed between the infrastructure manager and the person by whom the fee is payable or a person acting on his behalf, by an amount so determined.

6. In this Schedule:–

"common costs" means the costs incurred by the infrastructure manager in operating his railway infrastructure which are not attributable to the operation of trains on that infrastructure by any particular railway undertaking or international grouping;

"costs" include the cost of operating the control and safety systems, or providing or renewing capital assets, of a rate of return on capital invested in the infrastructure, of the payment of value added tax and administrative costs and other overheads; and

"infrastructure" means railway infrastructure.

SCHEDULE 2

Regulation 9(6)

THE INTERNATIONAL RAIL REGULATOR

Remuneration, pensions etc.

1.—(1) There shall be paid to a holder of the office of the International Rail Regulator such remuneration, and such travelling and other allowances, as the Secretary of State may determine.

(2) In the case of any such holder of the office of the International Rail Regulator as may be determined by the Secretary of State, there shall be paid such pension, allowance or gratuity to or in respect of him, or such contributions or payments towards provision for such a pension, allowance or gratuity, as may be so determined.

(3) If, when any person ceases to hold office as the International Rail Regulator, the Secretary of State determines that there are special circumstances which make it right that he should receive compensation, there may be paid to him a sum by way of compensation of such amount as may be determined by the Secretary of State.

(4) The approval of the Treasury shall be required for the making of a determination under this paragraph.

Staff

2.—(1) The International Rail Regulator may, with the approval of the Treasury as to numbers and terms and conditions of service, appoint such staff as the International Rail Regulator may determine.

(2) Where an employee of the International Rail Regulator who is (by reference to that employment) a participant in a scheme under section 1 of the Superannuation Act 1972**(a)** becomes a holder of the office of International Rail Regulator, the Treasury may determine that his term of office shall be treated for the purposes of the scheme as employment by the International Rail Regulator (whether or not any benefits are payable to or in respect of him by virtue of paragraph 1(2)).

Expenses of the International Rail Regulator and his staff

3. There shall be paid out of money provided by Parliament:–

(a) the remuneration of, and any travelling or other allowances payable under these Regulations to, the International Rail Regulator or to any staff of the International Rail Regulator;

(b) any sums payable under these Regulations to or in respect of the International Rail Regulator; and

(c) any expenses duly incurred by the International Rail Regulator, or by any staff of the International Rail Regulator, in consequence of the provisions of these Regulations.

(a) 1972 c.11.

Official Seal

4. The International Rail Regulator shall have an official seal for the authentication of documents required for the purposes of his functions.

Performance of functions

5. Anything authorised or required by or under these Regulations to be done by the International Rail Regulator may be done by any member of the staff of the International Rail Regulator who is authorised generally or specifically in that behalf by the International Rail Regulator.

Documentary evidence

6. The Documentary Evidence Act 1868(**a**) shall have effect as if:–
   (a) the International Rail Regulator were included in the first column of the Schedule to that Act;
   (b) the International Rail Regulator and any person authorised to act on behalf of the International Rail Regulator were mentioned in the second column of that Schedule; and
   (c) the regulations referred to in that Act included any document issued by the International Rail Regulator or any such person.

The Parliamentary Commissioner

7. In the Parliamentary Commissioner Act 1967(**b**), in Schedule 2 (departments and authorities subject to investigation) the following entry shall be inserted at the appropriate place:–
   "The International Rail Regulator".

Parliamentary disqualification etc.

8. In Part III of Schedule 1 to the House of Commons Disqualification Act 1975(**c**), the following entry shall be inserted at the appropriate place:–
   "The International Rail Regulator";
and the same insertion shall be made in Part III of Schedule 1 to the Northern Ireland Assembly Disqualification Act 1975(**d**).

SCHEDULE 3

Regulation 16

QUALIFICATIONS FOR INTERNATIONAL LICENCE

Good Repute

1. In determining whether a railway undertaking is of good repute the International Rail Regulator shall have regard to all relevant evidence, including any information in his possession as to the previous conduct of any appropriate officer of the undertaking if that conduct appears to him to relate to the undertaking's fitness to hold an international licence.

2. Without prejudice to the generality of his powers under paragraph 1, the International Rail Regulator shall not determine that a railway undertaking is of good repute if–
   (a) an order has been made by the court for the winding up of the undertaking or the sequestration of its estate under insolvency legislation or any director for the time being of the undertaking has been adjudged bankrupt or his estate has been sequestrated under that legislation or the undertaking or any such director has made a compromise with its or his creditors;
   (b) the undertaking or any appropriate officer of the undertaking has been convicted of a serious offence, including in particular an offence contrary to the law relating to commercial transactions, the law relating to transport, or social and labour law (including legislation relating to occupational health and safety); or
   (c) the undertaking or any appropriate officer of the undertaking has been convicted repeatedly of offences contrary to social or labour law not falling within sub-paragraph (b).

(**a**) 1868 c.37.
(**b**) 1967 c.24.
(**c**) 1975 c.24.
(**d**) 1975 c.25.

3.—(1) For the purpose of paragraph 2 a person has been convicted of a serious offence if that offence was committed under the law of any part of the United Kingdom or under the law of a country or territory outside the United Kingdom and if on conviction there was imposed on him for that offence a punishment falling within sub-paragraph (2).

(2) The punishments are–

(a) a sentence of imprisonment for a term exceeding three months;

(b) a fine exceeding level 4 on the standard scale;

(c) a community service order requiring him to perform work for more than 60 hours; and

(d) in the case of an offence committed under the law of a country or territory outside the United Kingdom, any punishment corresponding to those mentioned in paragraphs (a) to (c).

(3) In sub-paragraph (2)–

(a) the reference to a sentence of imprisonment includes a reference to any form of custodial sentence or order, other than one imposed under the enactments relating to mental health; and

(b) "community service order" means an order under section 14 of the Powers of Criminal Courts Act 1973(**a**) or under the Community Service by Offenders (Scotland) Act 1978(**b**).

4.—(1) Any reference in paragraph 3 to an offence under the law of any part of the United Kingdom includes a reference to a civil offence (wherever committed) within the meaning of the Army Act 1955(**c**), the Air Force Act 1955(**d**) or as the case may be the Naval Discipline Act 1957(**e**).

(2) For the purposes of paragraphs 1 to 4–

(a) convictions which are spent for the purposes of the Rehabilitation of Offenders Act 1974(**f**) shall be disregarded; and

(b) the International Rail Regulator may also disregard an offence if such time as he thinks proper·has elapsed since the date of the conviction.

5. In paragraphs 1 and 2 the reference to any appropriate officer of the undertaking is to any director, manager, secretary, or other similar officer of the undertaking or any person purporting to act in any such capacity.

Financial Fitness

6. Subject to paragraph 8 an applicant for an international licence shall be considered to meet the required standard of financial fitness when it can demonstrate that it will be able to meet its actual and potential obligations, established under realistic assumptions, for a period of twelve months from the date of application for a licence.

7. For the purpose of demonstrating its financial fitness a railway undertaking shall make available to the International Rail Regulator the undertaking's annual accounts, or if the undertaking is not able to provide annual accounts then the undertaking's balance sheet, together with details of the following matters (insofar as these cannot be ascertained from the annual accounts or, as the case may be, the balance sheet)–

(a) the railway undertaking's available funds, including the bank balance, pledged overdraft provisions and loans;

(b) the railway undertaking's funds and assets available as security;

(c) the railway undertaking's working capital;

(d) relevant costs, including the railway undertaking's purchase costs of payments to account for vehicles, land, buildings, installations and rolling stock; and

(e) charges on the railway undertaking's assets; and

(f) such other information concerning the financial fitness of the railway undertaking as the International Rail Regulator may reasonably request.

8. The International Rail Regulator shall not find the railway undertaking to be financially fit if the railway undertaking has substantial arrears of taxes or social security payments which are owed as a result of the undertaking's activity.

(**a**) 1973 c.62.
(**b**) 1978 c.49.
(**c**) 1995 c.19.
(**d**) 1955 c.19.
(**e**) 1957 c.53.
(**f**) 1974 c.53.

9. Without prejudice to paragraph 7(f), the International Rail Regulator may request that the railway undertaking provide to him audit reports or other suitable documents as the International Rail Regulator considers necessary in relation to the matters listed in paragraph 7(a)–(e) which have been prepared by a body other than the railway undertaking such as a bank, building society, accountant or auditor.

Professional Competence

10. For the purposes of these Regulations the requirements of professional competence are satisfied by a railway undertaking when:–

(a) the undertaking has or will have a management organisation which possesses the knowledge and experience necessary to exercise safe and reliable operational control and supervision of the type of operations specified in the licence;

(b) its personnel responsible for safety, in particular the drivers of the rolling stock, are fully qualified for their field of activity; and

(c) its personnel, rolling stock and organisation can ensure a high level of safety for the services to be provided.

11. A railway undertaking shall provide to the International Rail Regulator such information as he may reasonably require to enable him to determine, after consultation with the Health and Safety Executive, whether the requirements in paragraph 10 have been satisfied.

12. The information referred to in paragraph 11 shall in all cases include–

(a) particulars of the nature and maintenance of rolling stock, in particular as regards safety standards; and

(b) particulars of the qualifications of personnel responsible for safety and details of personal training including appropriate written proof of compliance with qualification requirements.

Insurance Cover

13.—(1) An applicant for an international licence shall be considered to meet the requirement of insurance cover where in accordance with the law of the United Kingdom and any relevant international law the undertaking maintains adequate insurance cover, or has made arrangements having equivalent effect, covering its liabilities in the event of accident to passengers, luggage, freight, mail and third parties.

(2) In sub-paragraph (1) "international law" means any provisions contained in any international agreement or arrangement to which the United Kingdom is a party and which have the force of law in the United Kingdom.

EXPLANATORY NOTE

(This note is not part of the Regulations)

These Regulations implement Council Directive 91/440/EEC of 29 July 1991 (OJ No. L237, 24.8.91, p. 25) on the development of the Community's railways and Council Directives 95/18/EC and 95/19/EC of 19 June 1995 on the licensing of railway undertakings and on the allocation of railway infrastructure capacity and the charging of infrastructure fees (OJ No. L143/75, 27.6.95, p. 70–75). They revoke the Railways Regulations 1992 and the Railways (Amendment) Regulations 1994 (which originally implemented Council Directive 91/440/EEC), and amend certain provisions of the Railways Act 1993 in relation to licensing of operators of railway assets and access rights. With the exception of paragraphs 6 to 8 of Schedule 2, the Regulations do not apply to Northern Ireland.

The Regulations require any railway undertaking which is also an infrastructure manager to prepare and maintain accounts separately for the provision of transport services and infrastructure management (regulation 5), and require any infrastructure manager to ensure that the expenditure on railway infrastructure he incurs does not exceed the income he

receives from infrastructure fees (regulation 6). They lay down requirements as to the fees to be charged by infrastructure managers for the use of railway undertakings who will in return provide the International Rail Regulator (appointed by the Secretary of State under regulation 9) with such information as he needs to determine whether fees are charged on a non-discriminatory basis (regulations 7 and 8 and Schedule 1).

The Secretary of State is empowered to appoint one or more infrastructure managers to be allocation bodies responsible for handling applications for railway infrastructure capacity (regulation 10). Detailed procedures for the handling of applications for infrastructure capacity are specified in regulation 11 where the application is made to an allocation body in Great Britain, and in regulation 12 where the application is made elsewhere in the European Union. Railway undertakings aggrieved by a decision of an allocation body may appeal to the International Rail Regulator (regulation 14).

The unlicensed provision of international services is made a criminal offence (regulation 15). The International Rail Regulator is appointed as the authority to issue international licences (regulation 16). Applicants for such licences must satisfy requirements as to good repute, professional competence, financial fitness and third party liabilities (regulation 16 and Schedule 3). Such licences are valid for as long as the licence holder complies with these Regulations and any licence conditions (regulation 18). The International Rail Regulator is empowered to monitor and suspend or revoke such licences in certain circumstances (regulation 19).

The Railways Act 1993 is amended to take account of the new access and licensing regimes established by the Regulations (regulation 21).

International groupings and railways undertakings are given statutory authority in respect of the provision of international services in exercise of rights granted under the regulations (regulation 22). Such groupings and undertakings are not to be common carriers in respect of the provision of such services (regulation 23). Certain enactments concerning railways are applied in respect of those services whether or not they would otherwise apply (regulation 24).

Any person affected by a refusal or failure to comply with obligations arising under the regulations referred to in regulation 26, and who suffers loss or damage caused by the refusal or failure, may bring a civil action, and the International Rail Regulator may seek to enforce compliance by civil proceedings for an injunction or interdict (regulation 26). It is an offence knowingly to provide false information under or for the purpose of the Regulations (regulation 27). The disclosure of information obtained under the Regulations is restricted in the same way as information obtained under the Railways Act 1993 (regulation 29).

This Statutory Instrument has been made in consequence of a defect in S.I. 1998/1340 and is being issued free of charge to all known recipients of that Statutory Instrument

STATUTORY INSTRUMENTS

1998 No. 1519

TRANSPORT

The Railways (Amendment) Regulations 1998

Made - - - -	*22nd June 1998*
Laid before Parliament	*23rd June 1998*
Coming into force	*27th June 1998*

The Secretary of State, being a Minister designated**(a)** for the purpose of section 2(2) of the European Communities Act 1972**(b)** in relation to measures relating to railways and railway transport, in exercise of the powers conferred by that section hereby makes the following Regulations:—

1. These Regulations may be cited as the Railways (Amendment) Regulations 1998 and shall come into force on 27th June 1998.

2.—(1) Regulation 21 of the Railways Regulations 1998**(c)** shall be amended in accordance with the following provisions of this regulation.

(2) In paragraph (2) after "After subsection (1)" insert "of section 6".

(3) In paragraph (4) for "of section 6 there shall be inserted" substitute "of that section insert".

Signed by authority of the Secretary of State for the Environment,
Transport and the Regions

Glenda Jackson
Parliamentary Under Secretary of State,
Department of the Environment,
22nd June 1998
Transport and the Regions

(a) S.I. 1996/266.
(b) 1972 c.68. By virtue of the amendment of section 1(2) of the European Communities Act 1972 by section 1 of the European Economic Area Act 1993 (c.51) regulations may be made under section 2(2) of the European Communities Act 1972 to implement obligations of the United Kingdom created or arising by or under the Agreement on the European Economic Area signed at Oporto on 2nd May 1992 (Cm 2073) and the Protocol adjusting the Agreement signed at Brussels on 17th March 1993 (Cm 2183).
(c) S.I. 1998/1340.

[DOT 11925]

EXPLANATORY NOTE

(This note is not part of the Regulations)

This instrument remedies a defect in the Railways Regulations 1998 by inserting a reference to section 6 of the Railways Act 1993 in regulation 21(2).